GLORIOUS
THINGS TO DO

For Grace Van der Velde, Megan, Ellen and Mary Kennedy, Evie Taylor, Claire Natasha Irwin, Esme Brook, Constance Swift and Kit and Lulu Pearson.

ROSEMARY DAVIDSON was brought up in County Down, Northern Ireland, along with her three sisters.

She now lives in London with her daughter Florence, twelve, and son Spike, nine, and works as an editor of books. She co-wrote with Sarah Vine the bestselling *The Great Big Glorious Book for Girls*.

GLORIOUS THINGS TO DO

Rosemary Davidson

Illustrations by Natacha Ledwidge

VIKING
an imprint of
PENGUIN BOOKS

VIKING

Published by the Penguin Group

Penguin Books Ltd, 80 Strand, London WC2R oRL, England

Penguin Group (USA) Inc., 375 Hudson Street, New York, New York 10014, USA

Penguin Group (Canada), 90 Eglinton Avenue East, Suite 700, Toronto, Ontario, Canada M4P 2Y3 (a division of Pearson Penguin Canada Inc.)

Penguin Ireland, 25 St Stephen's Green, Dublin 2, Ireland (a division of Penguin Books Ltd)

Penguin Group (Australia), 250 Camberwell Road, Camberwell, Victoria 3124, Australia (a division of Pearson Australia Group Pty Ltd)

Penguin Books India Pvt Ltd, 11 Community Centre, Panchsheel Park, New Delhi – 110 017, India

Penguin Group (NZ), 67 Apollo Drive, Rosedale, North Shore 0632, New Zealand (a division of Pearson New Zealand Ltd)

Penguin Books (South Africa) (Pty) Ltd, 24 Sturdee Avenue, Rosebank, Johannesburg 2196, South Africa

Penguin Books Ltd, Registered Offices: 80 Strand, London WC2R oRL, England

www.penguin.com

First published 2008

1

All Illustrations by Natacha Ledwidge unless otherwise stated below. Copyright © Natacha Ledwidge, 2008

Silhouettes and other illustrations by Dover Books used on the following pages: 11, 12, 13, 14, 15, 16, 17, 18, 19, 20, 21, 23, 24, 36, 39, 80 and 157

Illustrations copyright ©Kirsty Gordon, 2008. Images used on the following pages: 37, 127

Uncredited illustrations used on the following pages: 34, 35, 65, 66, 67, 68(bottom right), 69, 73, 75, 76, 81, 82, 83, 84, 85, 108, 109, 110, 111, 112, 113, 124, 125, 126, 138, 146, 147, 150, 151 and 152

The moral right of the author and illustrators has been asserted

Printed in Great Britain by Clays Ltd, St Ives plc

A CIP catalogue record for this book is available from the British Library

ISBN: 978-0-670-91768-6

CONTENTS

INTRODUCTION

There are those days when there just don't seem to be enough hours to fit in all the things you have to do – homework, room tidying, dish-washing – never mind all the things you'd like to do – creative schemes and projects, playing with friends or simply reading a book. Then there are those other days, long summer holiday days, when the hours seem to stretch empty and endlessly ahead, boredom looms and, listless and irritable, you cannot think of a single idea or thing that you'd like to do.

Glorious Things To Do is the book for just those days. Packed with brilliantly creative and constructive things to make, recipes and scientific experiments; there are ideas for things to do indoors and outdoors, things to do on your own, or with friends and family, and things for rainy days and for fine weather. And hopefully, some of these things will be so successful that you'll want to do them and make them, over and over again . . .

A Couple of Scientific Explosions

What better way to start a book of things to do than with a BANG. Here are two very safe, but very effective and dramatic, scientific explosions which you can do at home. They are pretty messy, so it would be best to do your experimenting outdoors.

COLA VOLCANO

* 1 litre bottle diet cola
* thick paper or flexible card
* 5 Mento mints

This is very messy, so make sure you do this where there is lots of open space for the cola to spray.

Open the bottle and put a small square of paper over the mouth. Make a tube out of another piece of paper just larger than the diameter of the mints. Put the tube on top of the square of paper directly over the bottle opening and drop in all the mints. Quickly slide the paper out from under the tube so the mints drop into the bottle. Almost immediately you will have a dramatic cola volcano. Any liquid left in the bottle (probably not a lot) will be delicately flavoured with mint.

What has happened? Cola is full of carbon dioxide gas. The water molecules in the cola attract each other and form a tight mesh (called surface tension) round each bubble of carbon dioxide. When the mints are dropped into the cola, the gelatine and gum arabic in them break this surface tension allowing the gas to escape. The surface of the mints is covered in thousands of small pits which are ideal places for the gas bubbles to form. As the mints sink to the bottom all this carbon dioxide pushes the liquid up out of the bottle in an absolutely spectacular way. The highest cola volcano has been recorded at 10 metres! Diet cola is used because it contains less sugar molecules than regular cola; sugar helps hold on to the carbon dioxide and results in a weaker reaction.

ALKA SELTZER EXPLODING FILM CANISTER

* 35mm plastic film canister with lid
* Alka Seltzer tablet
* tap water

Pop an Alka Seltzer tablet into the film canister and fill it about $^2/_3$ full with slightly warm tap water, quickly and firmly close the lid, put the canister on the table, lid end down, stand well back and wait for the dramatic results!

* If you use more than one tablet per canister, what do you think will happen?

* What happens if you vary the volume of water? Try it, and find out.

What has happened? As the tablet dissolves, carbon dioxide gas is formed. The gas pressure in the canister builds up – and eventually forces the lid off with a pleasing pop, sending the canister into the air.

Ten Birds Every Girl Should Know

Wherever you are, you'll have lyrical birdsong to greet the new day if you just listen out for it, and with practice you'll be able to spot and identify the birds living in your area effortlessly.

Birds are amazing creatures. Some migrate to warmer countries in the winter, flying as much as 7,000 miles without getting lost, and often returning to the place where they were born to nest the following summer. Other birds tell us when the seasons are changing by their song and the colour of their feathers. Some birds even alert us to danger by their call becoming more distressed or by simply disappearing to hide and shelter from a storm or from predators. If you look out of the window and can't see or hear any birds when there are normally many, you know that some kind of threat is on its way.

Here's how to identify some of the most common birds in the British Isles:

BLACKBIRD

✳ One of the most common British birds, you'll see them anywhere, from gardens to city car parks. A young blackbird has brown feathers and a brown beak, but after a couple of years males turn inky black and their beaks turn yellow. Females stay browner, with a more mottled breast. They are sprightly little birds about 25 centimetres long and you'll spot them running and hopping on the ground, typically advancing a few paces and then pausing before starting all over again. They are friendly and curious and will watch you intently with their little beady eyes.

Feeds on: seeds, fruit, insects and earthworms prised from the grass.

Song: unmistakably clear, rich and fluty, especially at the beginning of spring when you'll hear nothing more beautiful than a blackbird's song.

ROBIN

You can easily identify a robin from its red breast and very bright black eyes. The rest of the bird is olive-brown with a snowy white belly. They are the friendliest of birds and will hop quite near you when you are outside, flirting with their quick darting tails. If a robin gets to know you, he will become your friend and often follow you round the garden, watching and hoping you might find him a worm.

Feeds on: all kinds of insects and berries.

Song: a very beautiful clear ringing sound. A robin's song can often sound more subdued in autumn than it does in spring, when it is more confident and distinctly joyous.

HERRING GULL

The herring gull is one of the largest and most common gulls in this country, living all year round on and near the coast. Large, always squawking noisily and scavenging for any kind of food they can get their beaks on, you've probably seen them flying over rubbish tips. The adult herring gull can be identified by its light grey back, white underbelly and black wing tips. They are easily distinguished from other gulls by their pink legs and webbed feet.

Feeds on: everything and anything!

Song: if you have visited the seaside, you'll know their familiar call. They make a variety of sometimes annoying noises including a loud high-pitched yodelling and a scream that sounds a bit like a child crying.

JACKDAW

The jackdaw, a smallish member of the crow family, is black with a grey neck and black cap and is easily distinguished by its pale and outstanding eyes. Males and females look the same. Downright devious birds, they will seize any opportunity to do mischief, including stealing eggs from the nests of other birds. But you can't help but love these rogues and you'll spot them in both the city and the country.

Feeds on: insects, larvae, acorns and, occasionally, eggs or baby birds.

Song: a loud staccato call which sounds a bit like 'jack jack' and 'kaar kaar'.

KINGFISHER

✳ Quick, darting birds, you'll see a flash of their brilliant cobalt-blue wings if you're lucky enough to catch sight of one. They have bright orangey undersides, blue bars on their heads, an orange streak over their eyes and striking red legs. Kingfishers are found near lakes, rivers, canals or ponds; they like still or slowly flowing water. You'll rarely seem more than one at a time.

Feeds on: small fish and insects found in and over water.

Song: more of a shrill whistle, really, which sounds like 'chi-keeee'.

JAY

The prettiest member of the crow family. A shy bird, mostly found in and near woods, though occasionally you might see one popping up in the city. Jays have a smallish cinnamon-coloured body, black and white feathers on their heads, which can be raised into a crest, and a startling blue on their wings. Males and females look the same and are quite nervous, hopping with both feet together from branch to branch or along the ground.

Feeds on: insects, slugs, snails and worms and the occasional mouse; fruits, nuts and berries, particularly acorns, which you might see them burying and saving for the winter.

Song: a harsh, shrill note can you can hear from miles away.

SWALLOW

A small bird, about 20 centimetres long. It has blue-black wings and back (which looks black from above) and is chestnut on the underside, with a red throat and forehead. It's easily spotted by its graceful flight and unmistakable long forked tail. Males and females look similar, though males tend to have longer tail streamers. Swallows are migratory birds and the first arrivals mark the beginning of summer. In early September you will often see them gathering together sitting on overhead wires, preparing for their long journey to Africa, where they go for the winter.

Feeds on: insects caught on the wing.

Song: soft chirping twittering sound which is pretty, pure and clear.

KESTREL

The kestrel is probably the most common bird of prey in the British Isles. You'll often be able to see one hovering high in the air at the edges of motorways and other roads, searching for its prey with its powerful eyesight. Kestrels are mottled brown on the upper half, with darker tips at the end of their wings, and have a creamy-brown speckled belly. Females are slightly larger than males, who can be distinguished by their blue-grey head and tail. They live near farmland and suburbs.

Feeds on: small mammals, including mice and voles as well as small birds like larks, sparrows and finches.

Song: a twittering but strong 'kee kee' sound.

BUZZARD

* Another bird of prey and one of the most graceful and largest of British birds, with a wingspan of 115 centimetres. They are quite rare, mostly seen in Scotland and Wales, though you might just be lucky enough to see one in any rural and hilly countryside. A buzzard's feathers are a mottled rich-brown colour, with lighter creamy-brown markings underneath and long wings with distinctive dark ragged endings. They fly high, soaring in slow upward circles on updraughts of air.

Feeds on: small birds, mice, rabbits, even new-born lambs!

Song: a haunting mewling sort of sound, which it makes frequently.

MALLARD

* This is the wild duck from which all domesticated ducks are descended. Mallards are easy to spot swimming quietly on lakes or rivers. They are about 60 centimetres long and males have yellow beaks, bottle-green heads, white collars, chestnut breasts, as well as curled-up black tail feathers. Females are a dull streaky brown and grey with an orange bill.

Feeds on: seeds, plants, invertebrates.

Song: a deep, rasping note which sounds like 'quark' or 'dweek'. They also make a slightly softer, quacking sound.

BIRDS I HAVE SEEN

what	*when*	*where*
....	....	....
....	....	....
....	....	....
....	....	....
....	....	....
....	....	....
....	....	....
....	....	....
....	....	....
....	....	....
....	....	....
....	....	....
....	....	....
....	....	....
....	....	....
....	....	....
....	....	....
....	....	....
....	....	....
....	....	....

notes

....
....
....
....
....
....
....
....
....
....
....
....
....
....
....
....
....
....
....
....

COLLECTIVE BIRD NOUNS

Groups of birds often have very pretty and unexpected names. Try writing these down in your notebook and memorizing them, like a poem. Or you could paint some names on a large piece of paper and stick it up in your bedroom.

* ballet of swans
* band of jays
* brood of hens
* cast of hawks
* charm of hummingbirds
* colony of gulls
* concentration of kingfishers
* conspiracy of ravens
* flamboyance of flamingos
* flock of birds
* flush of mallards
* murder of crows
* paddling of ducks
* parliament of owls
* peep of chickens
* quarrel of sparrows
* tiding of magpies

* and finally . . . a clutch of eggs

Five Things to Do With Blackberries

The coming of autumn heralds early-morning starts and a return to school, but there's one last gift summer has to give. From the end of July until sometimes as late as October you will find delicious, plump blackberries in the hedgerows. Remember though — an old English story tells you not to pick blackberries after 10 October, when the devil pees on them!

✳ A blackberry is most delicious when picked on a hot day because the sugar content is at its highest.

✳ Take an umbrella with you so you can pull the faraway branches towards you – the ones other pickers won't be able to reach!

✳ Always rinse blackberries well before eating them, especially if you have picked them close to a road.

✳ If you are concerned about bugs, put all the blackberries in a bowl and cover them with cold water and a teaspoon of salt – any nasties will just float to the surface.

No doubt you'll tuck into the fresh blackberries with glee (best with a sprinkling of sugar and a dollop of cream or ice cream) but here are some other tasty ways to preserve and enjoy them.

1 BLACKBERRY JUICE

*

Pick the ripest berries, put them into a big bowl and crush them with something like a potato masher. Once you've pummelled them to a pulp, strain it through a fine sieve so you catch the tiny pips, and the juice drips cleanly into a saucepan below. Do this twice. Put the saucepan over a low heat, add sugar (about 4 tablespoons of sugar per ½ litre of juice) and bring it to the boil for 3 minutes. Wait until the liquid is cool then pour it into a clean bottle and keep it in the fridge. Drink it neat or dilute it with water, like a cordial. If you want to impress your friends, make a blackberry cocktail in a tall glass: half blackberry juice, half fizzy lemonade, with ice, slices of lemon or fresh mint leaves. Sip and gossip, preferably outside in the sun, and enjoy this deliciously refreshing drink.

2 BLACKBERRY JELLY

This is a wonder of nature, made from nothing other than blackberries – they don't even need cooking!

✳ Gather only the ripest, juiciest berries. Pummel and sieve them as for the blackberry juice above. Get some muslin (muslin is a fine cotton cloth – if you don't have any at home you can buy it from any haberdashery shop) and line the sieve snugly with a couple of layers, then pour the juice through it. Use a wooden spoon to squeeze the pulp of all its juice, leaving any pulp trapped in the muslin – you want the juice to be as clear as can be.

Pour into small jars – make sure they are very clean and absolutely dry before you fill them. Leave them in a warm place, like the airing cupboard, and they will miraculously set into a light jelly within a couple of hours. Spread it on scones, biscuits or bread and butter. If you want to keep the jelly for later, place a cut-out round of greaseproof paper over the top of the jelly jar, screw on the lid and store it in the fridge. It will only keep for about six weeks, so make sure you label the jar with a date.

3 BLACKBERRY JAM

Any kind of blackberries will do for this incredibly easy jam recipe. No exact quantities are needed and there is a simple way to judge how much sugar you need to use.

* Put the rinsed fruit into a bowl, making sure you've pulled out all the white hearts and any stems. Cover thoroughly with enough sugar so you can no longer see the blackberries in the bowl, and leave to soak overnight. The next day, put everything into a saucepan and bring it to a gentle boil for about half an hour – because of the sugar the fruit will get very, very hot, so be extremely careful not to touch it or spill any. After half an hour, check to see if the jam is ready and will set. To do this scoop out a small amount with a spoon and drop a tiny bit into a glass of cold water. If the mixture dissolves, boil it for a bit longer and keep checking every 5 minutes or so; when the jam stays together and hardens into a soft ball you can roll in your fingers, it is ready and you can take the mixture off the heat. Leave it to cool for about 2 hours.

Pour into clean jars (as described in the jelly recipe). The jam will keep fresh for up to a year, but do keep it in a cool, dark cupboard or the fridge once you've opened it to prevent mould forming. As well as spreading on bread or toast you can add this jam to plain yoghurt to make tasty blackberry yoghurt for breakfast.

4 BLACKBERRY AND APPLE CRUMBLE SERVES 4

This recipe is easy as pie!

For the filling
* 220g blackberries, well washed
* 4 large cooking apples, peeled, cored and sliced
* 75g caster sugar

For the crumble
* 175g plain flour
* 50g soft brown sugar
* 100g butter
* 50g ground almonds (optional but if using reduce the quantity of flour by 50g)

Preheat the oven to 190°C/gas mark 5.

Fill an oven-proof dish (the Pyrex glass ones are probably best) with alternate layers of apples, blackberries and sugar. Continue layering like this until you have used up all the fruit and sugar. Put the dish into the oven and cook for 20 minutes while you prepare the crumble.

Mix all the crumble ingredients together in a bowl, then – and this is the fun bit – dig into the mix with your clean fingertips and rub gently, as if you are tickling the mixture, until it looks like breadcrumbs. Put on some oven gloves, take the dish out of the oven and spoon the crumble mixture evenly over the top. Return it to the oven for another 30 minutes, on the same heat, and after this it will be ready to serve. The crumble tastes best with lashings of custard or ice cream. And in the unlikely event of leftovers, you can eat it cold, instead of cereal, for a hearty breakfast.

5 BLACKBERRY DYE AND A PRETTY PINK T-SHIRT

Blackberry dye is one of the oldest natural dyes known to man. You can dye anything from a T-shirt to an old cotton pillow case, but remember to dye pale or white things so that the natural purple-pink colour of the blackberries clearly comes through. Always make sure you use a natural fibre like cotton, otherwise the colour will wash out.

* You'll need a lot of fruit for this – about a kilo. The good news is that you can use all the blackberries which are not so good for eating – under-ripe, over-ripe, squashed or even those with a bit of mould on them, particularly when it's coming to the end of the blackberry season. Pick off the leaves and stems and put them into a big bucket. Crush and sieve them twice into a saucepan. Put in the T-shirt. Add enough water to cover it and turn on the heat and bring it to the boil, stirring all the time. Once it's boiling, immediately take the saucepan off the heat and leave it somewhere to rest for at least a day. Then, gently squeeze the excess liquid from the T-shirt and leave it to dry. It'll stay pink even after machine washing!

Book Binding

For every new writing project — whether it's a short story or a dream diary — you need a new notebook. But instead of buying one, why not make your own? It's a good way of recycling the leftover pages from an old exercise book or diary, and it's much more personal than a shop-bought one.

* You only need ten or twelve sheets of paper (don't use too many or it'll end up too thick). Next, choose a cover. This can be anything you like: perhaps plain brown paper for a practical workbook, wrapping paper, thin coloured cardboard or a picture from a magazine. Cut your chosen cover to the

same size as the paper pages, then make a neat
pile with the cover on the bottom and fold it all in
half – the crease down the centre makes the spine
of the book. Open the pages out flat again and,
using a pencil and a ruler, measure halfway down
the spine and make a small dot. Starting from
this middle point, measure out regular dots
about 1.5 centimetres apart along the length of
the spine.

figure 1

To sew your book together, use a fairly large
needle and some coloured thread about three
times the length of the spine. Punch a hole
through each dot using a drawing pin. Tie a knot
in the end of your thread, leaving a long end, and

figure 2

then, starting at the top, carefully sew down the spine, passing the needle down through one hole and up through the next (figure 1). When you reach the bottom, sew your way back to the top again, going down through the up holes and up through the down so the new stitches fill in the gaps between the existing ones (figure 2). When you reach the top, make an extra stitch, then tie the ends of the thread together and clip them short to finish off. Fold along the spine and you have your own hand-made notebook!

Catnip Mouse

There's nothing like catnip to make a cat's day — just a whiff of it and he'll be rolling around, leaping about and purring like mad. If you don't have a cat, never mind — you can always make a toy mouse for your best friend, or simply for the fun of it. Just leave out the catnip! To make a catnip mouse, you will need:

- * a 15cm square of felt
- * tracing paper
- * scissors
- * needle and thread
- * scraps of felt for the ears and tail
- * stuffing material (a pair of old tights will do)
- * dried catnip
- * black embroidery thread or wool

First, trace round figures 1 and 2 and cut two side pieces, so you have a left and a right side, and one belly piece out of the felt.

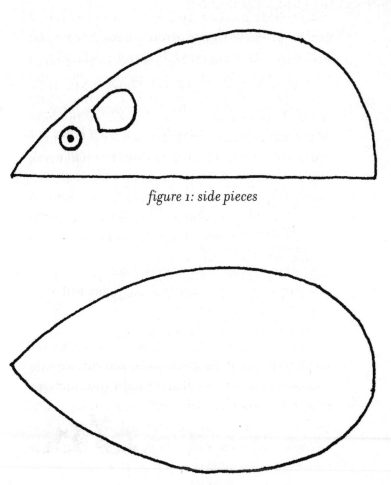

figure 1: side pieces

figure 2: belly piece

Put the side pieces together and oversew round the long, curved edge. Next, make the tail by cutting a thin triangle of felt, about 8 centimetres long and a centimetre wide at the base. Place the tail between the two side pieces, facing inside the body of your mouse, and sew it to the base of the mid seam where the sides join. Once the tail is tacked into place, open out the side pieces slightly and carefully fit the belly piece between them with the pointed end towards the nose of the mouse. Starting about 3 centimetres from the tail, oversew the sides and belly together, sewing round the blunt tail end, along the other side, round the pointy nose and 3 centimetres back along the first side. Tie your thread off, leaving a 4-centimetre gap.

Turn your mouse right side out so the seams are inside and push them gently so they stretch slightly (you might need to use a pencil to reach right inside the nose). Next, stuff your mouse — you can use a cut-up pair of old nylon tights. Use enough stuffing to keep the mouse in shape, but try not to over-stuff it or it'll end up looking like a round tennis ball. To make your mouse extra attractive to cats, mix a few pinches of catnip in with the stuffing. You can buy dried catnip in bags from some pet shops, or you can grow your own.

Once you've stuffed your mouse, turn the raw edges in slightly and oversew to close the gap. Give the tail a little tug, to make sure it's firmly attached. Cut two ear shapes out of felt and sew them in place, one on each side. Cut out two small felt circles for eyes and sew them on with black embroidery thread, using French knots (see page 65). Use more black embroidery thread to sew an X or O for a nose (if you feel inclined, you can add embroidery thread whiskers too). Sew a bell to the tail. You can make your mouse as simple or as elaborate as you please: just bear in mind your cat will probably destroy your careful handiwork in five minutes flat!

Cloudspotting for Beginners

Clouds consist of tiny droplets of water or ice crystals which are so small they can float in the air. Air contains water, but near the ground the water is usually in the form of an invisible gas called water vapour. When warm air rises, it expands and cools. Cool air cannot hold as much water vapour as warm air, so some of this vapour condenses and forms tiny droplets. When billions of these droplets come together they form clouds. Once you begin to understand the clouds why not do your own forecast? People have been doing this for centuries although even professionals get it wrong. That's another thing that is interesting about clouds – though sometimes predictable they have a mind of their own.

There are ten basic types of cloud, classified in terms of how high they are and their different shapes. They all have tricky Latin names but don't be put off: once you've mastered the basics, you'll spot each of them easily.

Low Clouds up to 2,000 Metres

1 CUMULUS

*
This is the cloud that looks like a clump of cotton wool – round at the top and flat on the bottom. It is known as the fair-weather cloud because it forms on sunny days. But these clouds can grow into towers and when they do they have the potential to develop into cumulonimbus clouds (see page 48), which are bad-weather and thunderstorm clouds.

2 STRATOCUMULUS

*
This cloud looks like mounds of candyfloss, with the sun shining through the gaps. It can be distinguished from the stratus cloud by its colour, which ranges from bright white to dark grey. Rain rarely occurs with stratocumulus clouds but they can indicate that bad weather is on the way.

3 STRATUS

* This is an indistinct layer of cloud in a grey tone with very little variation which usually covers the whole sky. It is the only cloud to regularly visit us at ground level, when it looks like light mist or drizzle.

Middle Clouds 2–5,000 Metres

4 ALTOCUMULUS

* A layer of small clouds, which looks a bit like a tray of grey dough balls about to go in the oven. When altocumulus form near mountains, they can sometimes look just like flying saucers. If they form on a warm and humid morning, it could mean thunderstorms are likely in the afternoon.

5 ALTOSTRATUS

* This is a boring cloud because it is normally just an indistinct grey-blue tone, covering the whole sky and hanging around for a long time. When the sun sets, however, it often transforms for a moment into something rather beautiful. Altostratus clouds often form ahead of rain, storms or even snowstorms.

Cirrocumulus

Cirrus

Altocumulus

Altostratus

Nimbostratus

Stratus

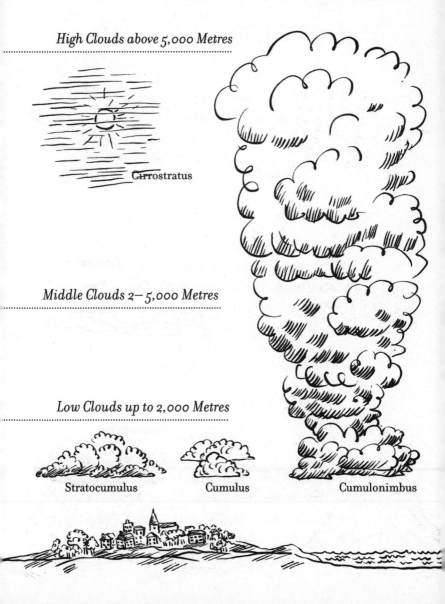

High Clouds above 5,000 Metres

Cirrostratus

Middle Clouds 2—5,000 Metres

Low Clouds up to 2,000 Metres

Stratocumulus   Cumulus   Cumulonimbus

High Clouds above 5,000 Metres

6 CIRRUS

＊ This delicate, wispy cloud is composed of falling ice crystals and is the most common and the highest of all the clouds. Cirrus clouds have a wavy appearance, and are named after the Latin word for a lock of hair. They are usually white and may indicate that fair and fine weather is on its way within the next 24 hours.

7 CIRROCUMULUS

＊ Small, white puffs that form in long, streaming rows. The small ripples in these clouds look a bit like the scales of a fish, which is why a large display of cirrocumulus clouds is known as a mackerel sky. They are rare, usually seen in winter, indicating fair but cold weather is on its way.

8 CIRROSTRATUS

✳ This cloud looks as though a white wedding veil has been placed over the entire sky. The cloud is so thin that the sun and moon can be seen through it. When it thickens to become whiter and then turns grey, it means rain might come within the next 48 hours.

Other Clouds

9 NIMBOSTRATUS

* These dark and ugly clouds can form at either a high, middle or low level. They are probably the most unpopular kind of cloud, since they mean nothing but rain, rain, rain.

10 CUMULONIMBUS

* The king of clouds. This is a huge, scary storm cloud. It often has the shape of a blacksmith's anvil and is associated with heavy rain, snow, lightning and all sorts of stormy and bad weather. The anvil usually points in the direction the storm is moving.

CLOUDS I HAVE SPOTTED

what	when	where

Crochet Flowers

Crochet is rather like knitting but instead of creating a line of stitches back and forth between two long needles, crochet uses just one short hooked needle to work a new loop through each individual stitch, before moving on to the next stitch in the sequence. It's easy enough to do, once you've got the knack, but you'll need a bit of patience and practice to get going. Just remember that all you are doing is creating an organized tangle of wool — if your first efforts end up a little bit more tangled than you'd like, it's only to be expected.

✳   It's generally best to use a thick needle for chunky wool, and a thin needle for fine wool. A 5mm crochet hook is about right for double-knitting wool. Once you've got your crochet hook and chosen a suitable ball of wool, you'll need to make a base chain. First, as with knitting, form a slip knot by making a loop in the yarn, drawing the tail halfway through the loop with your crochet hook, then pulling gently on both ends to draw the knot tight round the hook (figure 1).

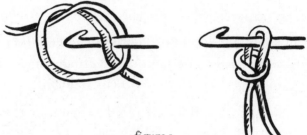

figure 1

Now, make a chain. Hold the crochet hook in your right hand, as if you were holding a knife, with your index finger resting on the slip knot. With your left hand, bring the yarn under the needle, then wrap it over, from right to left. This is called yarn over (yo). Next, turn the hook towards you so it catches the yarn, and pull it through the

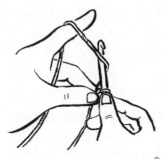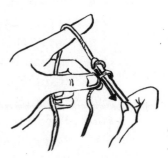

figure 2

original slip knot (or, pull the slip knot over the yarn) so the slip knot slides off and you're left with a new stitch on your hook (figure 2).

Keep hold of the yarn and the beginning of your crochet chain in your left hand. The trick is to get the tension of the yarn correct, so your stitches end up as neat loops, rather than being too loose and baggy, or too tight, like knots. Lots of good crocheters keep the yarn wrapped around their left index finger and hold the chain between their thumb and third finger. Because you use both hands for crochet, many left-handed people do it this way, too; experiment and see what feels

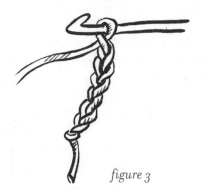

figure 3

comfortable. Keep repeating this process of yarn over and pull through, and you'll end up with a looped chain which is the starting point for all crochet stitches (figure 3).

Once you've mastered the chain, you'll want to build up your skills, and there's no better way than by crocheting a flower. They are pretty and simple to do – plus, they're made up of the kind of lacy loops and circles that are quite difficult to achieve with knitting, but are pretty straightforward with crochet. The problem is, doing crochet is a lot easier than describing how to do it. An abbreviated pattern is like algebra. On no account read the following set of instructions unless you're sitting with a crochet hook and a ball of wool in your hands ready to go. If you work through it as you go along, it'll soon make sense; if not, it'll be enough to put you off crochet for life.

You'll need two different colours of wool for your flower – one for the centre, one for the petals. Starting with the centre colour, make a chain of 6 loops (6 ch), then form the chain into a circle by sliding your crochet hook into the first loop,

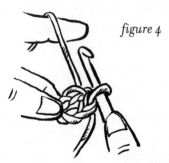

figure 4

yarning over and pulling the yarn through both the loop of the chain and the existing stitch, leaving one new stitch on the needle (figure 4). This is called a slip stitch (sl st).

Work one chain stitch – you'll need to do this at the end of every row – then make a single crochet (sc) into the 6-loop circle you've made, as follows: insert your crochet hook into the hole at the centre of the circle, yarn over, pull through the first stitch (that is, the chain that forms the edge of the circle), yarn over again, then pull through the remaining 2 stitches, to leave one stitch on your hook. Repeat 8 times and this will give you 9 single chain stitches, in a ring. Join the ends of the ring by making a slip stitch into your turning stitch, and prepare for the next round.

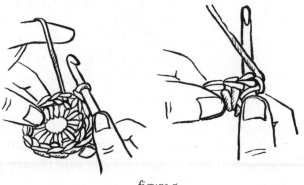

figure 5

Chain 1 to make your next turning stitch, then you'll need to make 2 single chains in each of the 9 chains in the ring. To do this, insert your hook beneath the V shape of the first stitch in the ring (figure 5). Yarn over and pull through, then yarn over again and pull through the remaining 2 stitches to make a new single chain. Insert your hook into the first single chain on the ring again (that is, pick up the same V) and make a second single chain; then, pick up the next V along and continue to make 2 single chains into each of the remaining 8 chains in the ring – you'll end up with 18 single chains in all. Join the second ring of stitches together by making a slip stitch into the turning chain, then fasten off your centre colour by cutting off your yarn (leaving a 10-entimetre tail), sliding the loop off the crochet hook, pulling the tail through the loop, and pulling tight.

Using the colour for the petals of your flower, insert your hook into the V of any one of the 18 single chains on your second ring of stitches, yarn over with the new colour leaving a tail of 10 centimetres, pull through, then make 2 chains, yarn over with the tail as well as the working length of wool to pull that first stitch tight. Then let the tail go, and work another 3 chains. ✳ Ignore the next two single chains in the ring, insert your hook in the V of the third and work a new single chain, then chain 4✳; repeat the instruction from ✳ to ✳ five times, then make a slip stitch into the third stitch of the first 6 chain. This should leave you with 6 petal-coloured loops round your centre (figure 6).

figure 6

Chain 1 to make your turning stitch, then start building up the petals themselves. First, make one single chain into the first petal loop, working into the hole of the loop itself (rather than any of the individual stitches). Next, working into the same loop, make a half double crochet (hdc) as follows: yarn over, insert your hook into the loop, yarn over again, and pull through; yarn over a third time, and pull through the remaining three stitches on the hook.

Working into the same loop, make a double crochet (dc): yarn over, pick up the loop, yarn over again, pull through; yarn over, pull through the first two stitches; yarn over a fourth time, and pull through the remaining two stitches on the hook.

Still working into the same loop, make a treble crochet (tc) as follows: yarn over twice, before inserting the hook into the loop, then yarn over again and pull through the first stitch, leaving four stitches on your hook; yarn over, pull through the next two stitches, leaving three on the hook; yarn over again, and pull through the next two stitches, leaving two on the hook; yarn over one last time, pull through the final two stitches, and you're done.

To complete the first petal, work your way back down through the stitches, making a treble crochet, then a double, then a half double, and finally a single, all into the same loop. Repeat this sequence of stitches – sc, hdc, dc, tc, tc, dc, hdc, sc – into each of the remaining five petal loops, then make a slip-stitch into the turning stitch you made all that time ago, and fasten off. You should be left with a pretty, six-petalled flower (figure 7).

figure 7

It looks indecipherable and yet, as you now know (having done it), it's actually quite easy. In fact, once you've crocheted your first flower, there'll be no stopping you. Darn in the tail ends, if you want to be neat, then use the finished flower to patch your jeans. Try making flowers with bigger centres, or with a different number of petals, pile them on top of one another and fix them together with a button. If you've made a whole stack of 6-petalled flowers, you can sew them in a line to make a scarf or join them together in groups, like patchwork (figure 8).

It's actually possible to crochet your flowers together as you go along, but that's a whole different set of instructions. It's not a problem, though: by the time you've made a dozen of them, you'll be so good at crochet, you'll be able to work it out for yourself.

figure 8

Abbreviated, the pattern would read as follows:

ch = chain

sc = single chain

hdc = half double chain

dc = double chain

tc = triple chain

sl st = slip stitch

Centre Colour:

ch 6, sl st into first to join

ch 1, 9 sc into loop, sl st to join – 9 stitches

ch 1, 2 sc into each sc, sl st to join – 18 stitches

fasten off

Petal Colour:

ch 6

* skip 2 sc, sc into 3rd sc, ch 4 *; repeat from
  * to * 5 times, sl st into 2nd st of 6 chain to
  join – 6 loops

ch1, * sc, hdc, dc, tc, tc, dc, hdc, sc into loop * ;
  repeat from * to * 5 times, then sl st to join

fasten off

Crystal Making

These crystals are so beautiful and so simple I guarantee you'll want to make them over and over again. The first method is more of a slow burner, so patience is required, but with the borax solution you'll see results almost immediately. Why not use letter shapes and make crystal letters to spell out your name?

METHOD ONE

* measuring cup
* boiling water
* clean jam jar
* 2 cups sugar
* nail
* string
* pencil

* Pour ½ cup of boiling water into the jam jar and gradually add the sugar, stirring well until it is dissolved. Attach the nail to one end of the string and the pencil to the other end. Put the pencil across the mouth of the jar so the nail hangs down into the sugar solution but does not touch the bottom. Put the jar in a warm place and leave for 2 or 3 days. The water will have evaporated and sugar crystals will have formed on the string.

METHOD TWO

* pipe cleaner
* clean jam jar
  or container
* boiling water
* metal spoon
* food colouring
* borax crystals
  (you can buy these
  in hardware shops
  or a large chemist)
* thread
* pencil

✳ Make a shape with your pipe cleaner that will easily fit inside your container – the first letter of your name or a heart, for example. Boil some water – if your container is made of glass put a metal spoon in it to prevent the glass from cracking – then pour in the water. Be very careful, or ask an adult to help with this bit. Add the borax, spoonful by spoonful, until no more will dissolve. (At this point you will see a layer of undissolved borax at the bottom of the jar.) Add a few drops of food colouring. Tie a piece of fine thread to your pipe-cleaner shape, tie the thread to a pencil, then suspend the shape in the borax solution, taking care it doesn't touch the sides or the bottom of the container. Three or 4 hours later, you will be able to see coloured crystals on your shape. Once the crystals have formed completely, take the pipe cleaner out of the solution very carefully. Spray gently with a furniture polish such as Pledge to protect and set the crystals.

Five Embroidery Stitches

Embroidery is a really great way to personalize your clothes and make extra-special gifts for your friends. Once you've dyed your T-shirt with blackberries, why not make it even more individual with your own embroidery patterns? You could even embroider your name. Here are some different stitches for you to use.

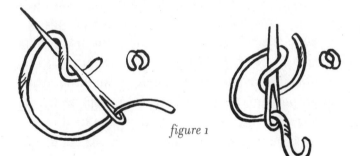

figure 1

1 FRENCH KNOTS

* Thread your needle, and tie a knot in the end of the thread. Then, bring the needle up through the fabric (figure 1). Gently pull the thread to the left, then put the needle flat on top of the thread and bring the thread over the needle from left to right. Tuck the thread back under the needle, from right to left, so it's wrapped anti-clockwise round the

needle. Without letting the loop of thread slide off, insert the needle back into the fabric, right next to where it came out. As you pull the needle through, keep one finger on the loop, holding it flat against the fabric. Gently draw the thread tight to leave a neat, ornamental knot.

2 CHAIN STITCH

Bring the needle through the piece of fabric at the beginning of your line of stitching (figure 2). Loop the thread forward, along the line you're going to sew, then insert the needle back into the fabric right next to where it came out. Bring the point of the needle back up through the fabric, one stitch on. Before you pull the needle through, tuck the thread under the point. Bring the needle through the fabric, and gently draw the thread tight, making a neat chain stitch. As a rough

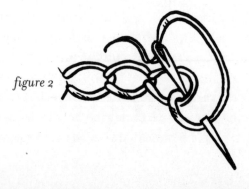

figure 2

guide, the width of the stitch should be about
²/₃ its length. Continue adding stitches until
you've worked the required length. If you sew
chain stitch in a tight spiral, it can be used to
colour in a circle.

3 FEATHER STITCH

Bring the needle through the fabric, and loop
the thread downwards, along the line you intend
to sew (figure 3). Insert the needle back into the
fabric, one stitch to the right, and bring the
point of the needle through diagonally, one stitch
downwards and to the left, to form a triangle. Tuck
the loop of thread under the point of the needle,
and pull the needle through, so that the thread
forms a V shape. The next stitch is made the same
way, but in the opposite direction: loop the thread
downwards, insert the needle one stitch to the
left, and bring the point of the needle through

figure 3

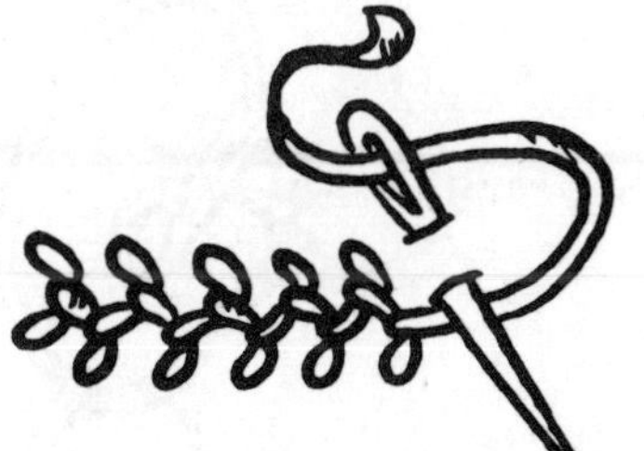

one stitch downwards and to the right, diagonally. Tuck the loop of thread under the point of the needle and pull through, so that the thread forms a V shape, interlocking with the first stitch. Repeat, alternating right and left stitches, until you've worked the required length.

4 DAISY STITCH

This is a variation on chain stitch – you can use it to make a lovely flower. Bring the needle through the fabric at the centre where you want the flower to be. Loop the thread round, and insert the needle back into the fabric, right next to where it came out (figure 4). Take one stitch, the length of one petal, and, tucking the loop of thread underneath the point of the needle, pull the thread gently through to make a neat loop. Take a tiny stitch over the top of the petal loop to hold it in place, then bring the needle back up through the fabric at the centre point, and repeat until you have the required number of petals.

figure 4

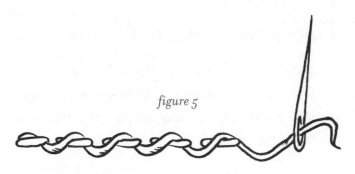

figure 5

5 WHIPPED RUNNING STITCH

* Sew a line of simple running stitch (figure 5). Using thread in a contrasting colour, bring the needle through the fabric at the start of the line of stitching, then – without putting the needle through the fabric – sew the new thread under each running stitch, from top to bottom, so it's wrapped around the existing stitching to create a corded look. This is one of the quickest ways to create a decorative line of stitching, and it's also an easy way to make a plain hem look pretty. The same technique can be used with backstitch.

Two Tricks with Water

Get these two tricks right, and your friends will be gasping with amazement. Practice makes perfect, though – make sure you do a trial run or you may be left in a soggy state!

TRICK ONE

* Carefully fill a wine glass to the brim with water. Put a piece of card (a square cut out from a cereal packet is ideal) on top so the card touches both the surface of the water and the glass. Hold the card carefully in place and turn the glass upside down, holding it by the stem. Take your hand away – the card will not drop off and the water won't spill!

What has happened? Air pressure outside the glass presses against the card keeping it tight to the rim so the water does not spill. If the glass isn't completely full, the air in the glass will press against the card causing it to fall off and the water to spill out. What a mess!

TRICK TWO

* Take two identical glasses or tumblers and fill each absolutely to the brim with water. Place a piece of card on top of the first glass, as in the first experiment, quickly turn this one upside down on top of the second filled glass, then carefully slide the card out from the middle of the two glasses (figure 1). Now, see how many two-pence coins you can slide between the glasses – on one side only. Add one . . . then very carefully see if you can slide another on top of the first coin. And, more risky still, can you try to add a third without the water pouring out of the gap? (figure 2).

What has happened? The surface tension of the water stops it from gushing out from the sides of the containers – even when a coin is inserted between the sides.

figure 1

figure 2

Three Guitar Chords and an Easy Song

If you can get your hands on a tuned guitar with all its strings attached, it's easy to learn a few chords, which is enough for a simple song. In fact, once you can play three chords in a row with confidence, there'll be no stopping you — many well-known bands have built entire careers on less!

All you need to know is that each chord is named after a musical note — E, D and A, for example — and that, while a chord diagram might look like a strange pattern of lines and dots, it's actually just a straightforward picture of where to put your fingers on the guitar strings. Opposite is the diagram for A (figure 1). The six vertical lines are the six strings of the guitar, with the long neck of the guitar pointing up, and the round body at the bottom. As you look at the guitar, the fattest string (1) is on the left, the thinnest string (6) is on the right. The shorter, horizontal lines are the little metal bars that run across the neck of the guitar (these are called frets). The dots represent

A

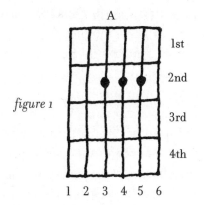

1st

2nd

figure 1

3rd

4th

1 2 3 4 5 6

the fingers of your left hand (you'll be using your right hand for strumming). You will need to put your fingers on the neck of the guitar in the gaps between the frets, and press down on each string firmly with your fingertips.

Sit with the guitar in your lap, holding the neck loosely in your left hand with your thumb resting gently against the back and your fingers curled round the neck (but not touching the strings yet). The fattest string (1) will be at the top, the thinnest (6) at the bottom. Strum a few times by drawing the fingers of your right hand lightly over the strings from top to bottom across the body of the guitar. Remember what this sounds like.

Now, try your first chord. Imagine each finger of your left hand has a number (figure 2). For A (figure 1), your fingers go in the second gap between the frets: your first finger goes on string 5, your second finger on string 4 and your third finger on string 3, so they are all together in a row. Strum from top to bottom with your right hand, and see if you can hear the difference. If the strings sound buzzy, press down on them a bit harder – that should fix it. Strum a few more times: you'll find yourself playing a sweet, tuneful chord in the key of A. (If it sounds discordant or jarring, there's something wrong – perhaps your guitar is out of tune, or your fingers are in the wrong place. It's probably best to work out what the problem is now, before you go any further, if only for the sake of those around you who might have to listen to your efforts.)

figure 2

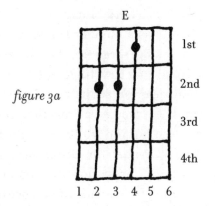

figure 3a

Now for chords E and D (figures 3a and 3b). Remember – these diagrams are just pictures of your fingers on the strings of the guitar! For these two chords, you'll find it's more comfortable to have your fingers in the shape of a triangle, rather than in a row.

For E, put your second finger on string 2 and your third finger on string 3, both in the second gap between the frets, then put your first finger against string 4 in the first gap (towards the top of the guitar neck). Strum down across all six strings, and hear what it sounds like.

For D, your first finger goes on string 4 and your second finger on string 6 in the second gap between frets; your third finger goes on string

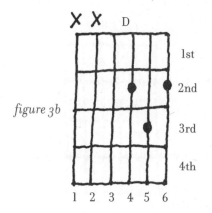

figure 3b

5 in the third gap towards the body of the guitar. An X in the diagram means don't play this string – when you strum the chord for D be careful to miss out the first two strings or it'll sound wrong (try it, and see what you think).

Play each chord on its own, then switch between chords – aim to get the change as smooth as possible, without too many long pauses. It's worth persevering: once you've got the hang of it, you can do a lot with these three chords. To start with, A, D and E form the basis for a simple blues song: play them in sequence (A, D, A, E, D, A); make up some lyrics about how, since your baby left you, you've been crying all the time and how, if your baby don't come back, you'll surely end up dyin' (or something along those lines); put them together and you'll feel like Muddy Waters in no time!

If you're in a more traditional mood, here's a lovely old song you can play instead:

'EARLY ONE MORNING'

         A   D   E
Early one morning, just   as the sun was   rising,

            A   D   A
I heard a maiden singing from the   valley   below.

  E   D   A   E   D   A
Oh, don't   deceive   me,   oh, ne-   -ver leave   me,

    A   D   E   A
How could you   use a   poor maiden   so?

        A   D   E
Gay is the garland and   fresh are the   roses I've

        A   D   A
culled from the garden to   bind on thy   brow.

  E   D · A   E   D   A
Oh, don't deceive   me,   oh, ne-   -ver leave   me

    A   D   E   A
How could you   use a   poor maiden   so?

Irish Wheaten Bread

This bread is amazingly easy to make. You don't need to do any complicated fiddling about with yeast or endless kneading of the dough for it to work, and it is truly delicious with some butter and raspberry jam.

For two loaves you will need:

* large baking tray or 2 x 450g loaf tins
* large mixing bowl
* 350g strong wholemeal flour
* 175g strong plain flour
* 1 tsp salt
* 1 tbsp caster sugar
* 2 tsp bicarbonate of soda
* 2 x 284ml cartons buttermilk or natural yoghurt

Preheat the oven to 200°C/gas mark 6.

Grease the loaf tins or baking tray.

Sift the flours, salt, sugar and bicarbonate of soda into a large mixing bowl. Gradually add between 400 and 450ml of buttermilk or yoghurt, just enough to form a soft but not too sticky dough. Mix briskly and then gather the dough into a ball. Knead lightly on a floured surface, until it becomes smooth. Divide the dough in half, form it into rounds and put them either on a baking sheet or in the loaf tins. Cook the bread on the top shelf of the oven for 30 minutes. Turn the oven down to 180°C/gas mark 4 and cook for 10–15 minutes longer.

The bread is ready when nicely risen and crusty on the surface – it should also make a pleasing hollow sound when you tap it on the bottom. Remove from the baking sheet or tins and allow to cool on a wire rack.

It can be eaten right away or it will keep for two to three days, loosely wrapped in foil.

How to Make a Diamond Kite

A breezy day is perfect for kite flying, and if you make your own you can have the satisfaction of looking up at your own creation swirling through the air.

* 2 x 6mm wooden dowels, from a hardware shop – one 90cm long, one 102cm long
* ruler
* pencil
* scissors
* string
* sharp penknife or Stanley knife
* glue – you'll need a strong wood glue as well as Pritt Stick.
* 50m nylon cord
* 102cm-square sheet of brown paper,
* paint, ribbons and anything else you might need to decorate your kite

The two sticks are going to form a cross, with the shorter stick placed horizontally across the longer one. They need to cross exactly in the centre so measure 45 centimetres on the horizontal stick and mark it with a pencil. Do the same with the vertical stick – making the mark at the halfway point of 51 centimetres. Carefully, with the knife, take a small scoop of wood out of each cross point, so when the sticks are put together they will fit snugly (figure 1).

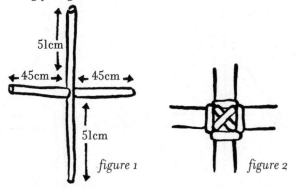

51cm

←45cm→ ←45cm→

51cm

figure 1   *figure 2*

Put a blob of strong glue on each stick at the scooped-out cross point and stick them together, making sure they are at right angles to each other. Wait for the glue to dry and then carefully tie the sticks tightly together with the nylon cord, to ensure they are very firmly fixed in this position (figure 2). This is the frame of the kite.

Carefully cut a notch at the very end of each of the four cross bars, cutting it just deep enough for the nylon cord to fit into. Cut off a piece of the cord about 150 centimetres long and stretch it round the four corners of the frame, looping it tightly over each of the notches. You want the cord to be taut but not so tight it bends the frame or distorts the perfect right angles of the cross. Finish by wrapping it round and knotting it off at the final notch, cutting off any cord that you don't need (figure 3).

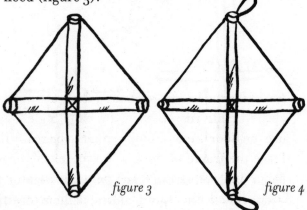

figure 3   *figure 4*

Cut two 15-centimetre pieces of cord and knot each one into a loop, attaching one round the notch at the top of the kite and the other at the bottom (figure 4).

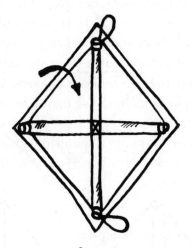

figure 5

Next take the brown paper and flatten it out on a cleared table (if you haven't a table big enough, use the floor). You want the paper to be really flat. Place the frame of the kite on top of the brown paper and with a ruler and pencil draw straight lines round the kite, leaving a 3-centimetre margin. Then cut out the brown paper with your scissors. Fold the edges over the nylon frame and glue them down so the paper covers the whole frame tightly. Be sure to leave the string loops at the top and bottom of the kite free (figure 5).

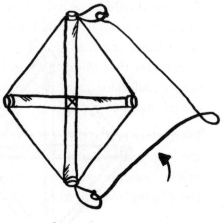

figure 6

Cut a piece of string 120 centimetres long and tie one end to the loop at the top of the kite and the other to the loop at the bottom. Tie another small 15-centimetre loop in the string at the halfway point, so it will be in line with the intersection of the two cross sticks. This will be the kite's bridle: the string to which the flying line is attached (figure 6).

Here's the fun bit. Make a tail for the kite by cutting off about a metre of cord and tying on small pieces of ribbon at regular intervals along it, about 10 centimetres apart. Attach this pretty tail to the loop at the bottom of the kite (figure 7).

The kite should be as light as possible, so try not to weigh the tail down with too much ribbon or other heavy material. Now you can decorate it. Remember that when the kite is flying you will see its underside from the ground, so you could colour that too.

Tie the free end of the rest of the nylon cord onto the loop you've made at the centre of the kite's bridle. Keep the nylon cord on its roll – this is the kite's flying line and reel.

All you need now is a windy day. Go fly your kite!

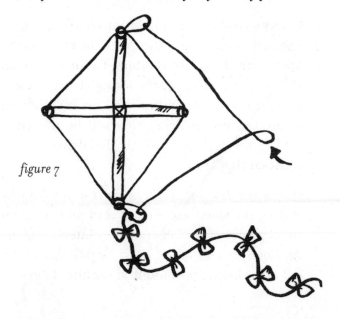

figure 7

DESIGNING MY DIAMOND KITE

* Use this template to design your own kite, and why not personalize it by adding your own patterns and colours.

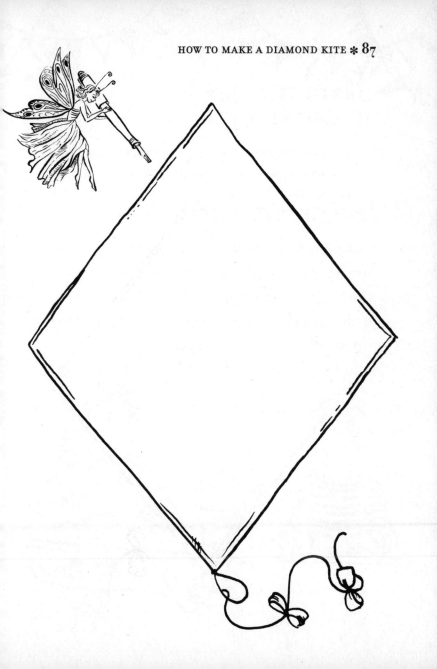

Ice-Cream Parties

It's hard to find a really good knickerbocker glory or banana split in cafés and restaurants these days — which is such a shame because they are delicious to eat and also just such good words to say. Fortunately they are great fun to make at home.

KNICKERBOCKER GLORY
SERVES 2

The knickerbocker glory is a classic ice-cream parlour dessert, first made popular in the 1930s. There isn't really a set recipe, so you can use your imagination and invent your own version. Serve it in a tall sundae glass or, if you don't have one, use a tall glass tumbler instead. You can vary the recipe by adding jelly, different fruits, a chocolate sauce or strawberry syrup — anything goes. A nice fan-shaped wafer adds a special finishing touch.

For the knickerbocker glory

* fresh fruit of your choice, sliced
* 200g sponge cake or 1 meringue per person — broken up
* 200g ice cream per person — vanilla, chocolate or strawberry, or a scoop of all three
* 200ml cream, whipped to form peaks
* 80g flaked almonds, lightly toasted
* ½ chocolate flake, crumbled
* wafer fan
* fresh strawberry

For the chocolate sauce
- * 225g plain chocolate
- * 150ml milk
- * 75ml double cream
- * 40g sugar

* First make the chocolate sauce. Break the chocolate into small pieces in a glass bowl. Put the bowl in a saucepan of water, and heat until the chocolate has melted. Take care that no water bubbles up and splashes into the bowl. In a separate pan, bring the milk, cream and sugar to simmering point. Pour this into the melted chocolate and stir until the mixture is smooth and glossy. Cover and set aside.

Put fruit, sponge cake or meringue, chocolate sauce and ice cream in four glasses in layers until they are three-quarters full. Spoon the whipped cream on top, and garnish with a sprinkle of toasted almonds and chocolate flake. Add a wafer fan and a fresh strawberry to decorate – and voilà!

BANANA SPLIT SERVES 2

For chocolate sauce – see knickerbocker glory.

* banana, cut in half lengthways
* strawberry, vanilla and chocolate ice cream
* whipped cream
* flaked almonds, toasted (optional)
* a dash of lemon juice

* Prepare the chocolate sauce and set aside.

Sprinkle the halved banana with lemon juice (to stop it browning). Put it on a plate, add a scoop of each ice cream and pour over the chocolate sauce. Top with cream, sprinkle with toasted almonds and serve.

BUTTERSCOTCH SAUCE FOR ICE CREAM SERVES 4-6

* 75g butter
* 225g brown sugar
* 140ml double cream
* 1 tbsp golden syrup

Melt the butter in a small heavy saucepan over a low heat. Stir in the sugar, cream and syrup. When the sugar has dissolved, bring the mixture to the boil. Allow to cool a little before serving.

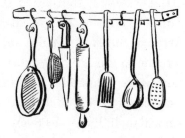

BAKED ALASKA SERVES 4-6

Also known as omelette surprise! How can you bake ice cream without it turning into a puddle in the oven? The secret is to encase the ice cream in meringue completely before baking in a VERY HOT oven.

* 4 egg whites
* 225g caster sugar
* 18cm thin flan sponge cake (these can be bought pre-baked in supermarkets)

* 250g chopped fruit, such as strawberries or raspberries (optional)
* 250ml block vanilla ice cream

* Preheat the oven to 230°C/gas mark 8.

To make the meringue whisk the egg whites until very stiff and fold in the caster sugar. Put the sponge on a shallow baking dish or ovenproof plate. Arrange the fruit on the sponge and put the ice cream on top. Pile the meringue over the ice cream with a spatula, making sure it is completely covered — if you leave any gaps the ice cream will melt. Put in the oven and cook for about 10 minutes, or until the meringue has browned to a golden colour. Eat immediately.

WHO TO INVITE TO
MY ICE-CREAM PARTY

name
....

name
....

....
....

....
....

....
....

....
....

....
....

....
....

....
....

....
....

....
....

....
....

....
....

....
....

....
....

....
....

....
....

....
....

....
....

MY DREAM ICE-CREAM PARTY

notes

....

....

....

....

....

....

....

....

....

....

....

....

....

....

....

....

....

....

Impossible Pie

SERVES 6-8

This recipe is so simple and is nothing short of miraculous. You don't have to faff about making pastry — just throw all the ingredients into a large bowl, stir it all together, then pour it into a greased pie dish and bake, and lo and behold, you have an impossible pie, crust and all, but without the fuss. It's an Australian recipe, so maybe that's why it seems upside down and back to front — but it works. Perhaps it's something to do with gravity.

* 140g plain flour
* 500ml milk
* 225g sugar
* 85g desiccated coconut
* 4 eggs, beaten
* vanilla essence
* finely grated rind and juice of one lemon
* Greek yoghurt or crème fraiche or double cream
* selection of berries and/or other fruit

* Preheat the oven to 180°C/gas mark 4. Grease a 25cm ceramic pie dish.

With a wooden spoon, slowly mix together all the ingredients, except the last two, in a large mixing bowl until blended. Pour into the pie dish and bake for about an hour. Allow to cool in the dish before turning it out. Serve with yoghurt, crème fraiche or double cream and berries or other fruit.

Magnetic Balloon

These are great examples of static electricity at work – surprise your friends with a balloon and your new magical powers.

* Pour some Rice Krispies onto a plate. Rub the balloon on a wool jumper 5 or 6 times. You might hear it crackle and feel the hairs stand up on your arms. Hold the balloon 5 centimetres above the Rice Krispies. They will jump up and stick to the balloon.

If you rub the balloon on your jumper and then hold it over someone's head, you can make their hair stand on end.

Rub the balloon again and you should be able to make it stick to the wall due to the static charge.

Make a Wish

Sadly, twinkling fairy godmothers or genies who appear from lamps to grant us three wishes are a rare occurrence in real life, but that doesn't mean you can't find opportunities to make wishes aplenty, every day of your life, if the fancy takes you.

Remember, close your eyes when you are making your wish, and don't tell it to anyone — you'll stand a better chance of it coming true.

WISHING ON A STAR OR A SHOOTING STAR

In winter, when it gets dark early, look up at the sky as you walk home from school. It is said that a wish can be made on the first star you see twinkling in the heavens. You can also wish on a shooting star, if you are ever lucky enough to see one. Before you make your wish, say this little poem:

> *Star light, star bright*
> *First star I see tonight,*
> *I wish I may, I wish I might*
> *Have the wish I wish tonight.*

WISHBONES

The wishbone is the thin V-shaped bone found at the top of the breast in a roast chicken or turkey. Put the wishbone to dry in a safe place after lunch or dinner – for several hours, or overnight if you are patient enough to wait that long. When it is quite dry the bone will be brittle and will break more easily.

✽ Find someone to pull the wishbone with you – the traditional way is for each person to hook their little finger tightly round one half of the bone; then, when you are ready, pull. When the bone breaks, whoever is left holding the largest half of the wishbone may make a wish.

BIRTHDAY CANDLES

* This is the best-known occasion for making wishes. Take an extra-deep breath, and try hard to blow out all the candles on your cake in one big puff, then make your wish.

SNEEZING

* In France, when someone sneezes, instead of saying 'Bless you!' they say 'A tes souhaits!' which means 'To your wishes!' So next time you sneeze, make a wish.

WISHING WELLS

* Throw a penny in a wishing well, or a fountain, then make a wish. The most famous of all wishing fountains is the Trevi fountain in Rome. But if you can't make a trip to Rome, look out for wishing wells in parks or fountains in town.

WHAT I AM WISHING FOR

Nettles

It may take a few stings and a bit of effort, but nettle soup home-made and from hand-picked nettles is surprisingly tasty and healthy, too. You don't need to worry too much about the stings because, as practically everyone knows, the best cure is dock leaves, which you'll always find near the offending nettle. Just scrunch up the fresh leaves and rub them onto the skin, and this will immediately cool and dull the pain. Once you know how to do this you can be fearless in search of the best nettles. Put on some gloves, tuck your jeans into your socks, arm yourself with dock leaves and have a good root round.

The best time to make nettle soup is in early spring when the short young shoots are succulent and most flavoursome. Pick the palest new green leaves from the top of the plants. Don't pick them after about the beginning of June because the leaves become tough and bitter.

NETTLE SOUP SERVES 4

- * 3 tbsp olive oil
- * 1 large onion, chopped
- * 2 large potatoes, peeled and chopped into cubes
- * 750ml vegetable or chicken stock
  (fresh is always best but cubes will do)
- * 30 nettle shoots (about 6 leaves to a shoot)
- * 250ml milk
- * salt and pepper

* Heat the olive oil in a saucepan and add the chopped onion. Fry gently for about 10 minutes until the onion becomes soft and transparent. Add the potato and cook for a couple more minutes, then pour in the stock. Bring to the boil, add the nettles, and simmer the soup for about 20 minutes, until the potatoes are soft.

Take the saucepan off the heat and leave it to cool for about 15 minutes, then blend. A hand blender is best, but a liquidizer will also do. Whizz the mixture until it is a smooth purée. Put back on the heat, add the milk, some freshly ground pepper and a couple of pinches of salt, to taste. Serve with hot toast and butter for a heart-warming lunch or supper.

Newspaper Beads

These beads, made from old newspaper or magazines, are easy to make and a fun way to spend a wet afternoon. When you have made enough beads, thread them onto some string to make a unique necklace or bracelet, or glue them to a disc of stiff card to make a brooch.

* sheets of newspaper, comics or magazines
* ruler
* pencil
* scissors
* knitting needle
* craft glue
* various coloured paints (optional)
* string, wool or thread

* With your ruler and a pencil, make marks at 3-centimetre intervals all the way down the left-hand side of a sheet of newspaper. Then, starting 1.5 centimetres down from the top on the right-hand side, make marks 3 centimetres apart. Connect the marks on the left-hand side with the two opposite on the right to make long, thin triangles. Cut the triangles out.

Starting at the wide end, keep winding the paper triangles tightly round the knitting needle until you are almost at the pointed end. Hold the paper in place and apply a thin layer of glue to the rest of the triangle then continue to wind until the triangle point is securely glued. Slide the paper bead off the knitting needle and leave it to dry.

When they're dry, the beads can be painted. If you used colour magazines or comics to make the beads they may already have interesting colours or patterns.

Origami Crane

Origami is an ancient Japanese technique. Its name comes from ori (or oru) meaning fold, and kami (or gami) meaning paper. Through origami, you can take a square piece of paper and turn it into a flower, a bird or a box, without using any glue and without cutting the paper: you just make a series of folds. It's very simple, very elegant and (when you get it right) very beautiful.

As with all origami you start off with a square of paper. You can buy special origami paper, which is coloured or patterned on one side, but any kind of paper will do as long as it's quite thin and square.

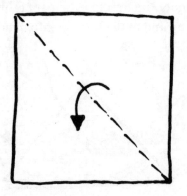

figure 1a

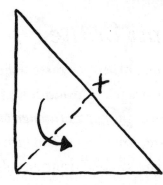

figure 1b

Place your paper with the patterned side down. Fold the square in half to make a triangle (figure 1a) and then fold a second time to make a smaller triangle (figure 1b).

With what used to be the centre of your paper at the top (X on figure 2a), fold the top flap back on itself to the left then open it again, leaving a crease. Putting your finger at the base of this crease under the first layer of paper, bring the top triangle up and to the left, opening and flattening

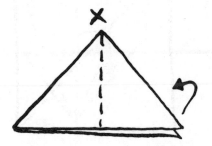

figure 2a

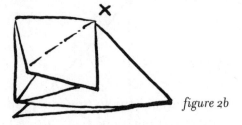

figure 2b

it down to form a neat square (figure 2b). Turn over and repeat the process, this time to the right, to create another square right on top of the one you have just made.

With the X at the top, and working on the front square only, fold the outside edges into the middle to make a kite shape. Bend the little triangle at the top backwards and forwards, forming a crease (figure 3a). Then (and this is the fiddly bit)

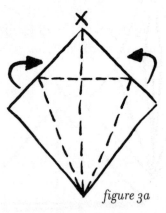

figure 3a

carefully pull the bottom corner upwards, opening the paper out along the existing folds, to make a long diamond shape (figure 3b). Turn over and repeat on the other side.

You will now have a long diamond that looks like it has two legs, which should point down. Working on the top layer of paper only, fold the outside edges into the middle (figure 4a); turn over, and repeat on the other side.

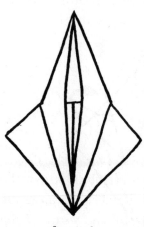

figure 3b

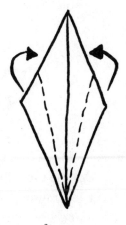

figure 4a

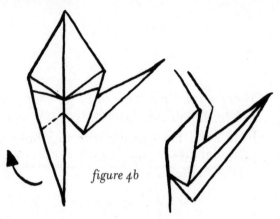

figure 4b

Fold the two long points at the bottom upwards and sideways, folding them back on themselves so the crease is tucked neatly inside the 'body' (figure 4b). These points form the neck and tail of your crane.

figure 5

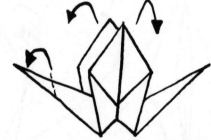

Use the same folding-inwards technique to make a fold towards the end of the neck, forming the crane's beak, then gently pull the wings of the crane apart (figure 5).

There's one final trick to bring your paper bird to life. If you turn it onto its back, you'll see a little hole: blow gently into this hole, and the body will inflate (figure 6).

Outdoor Games

As well as the well-known classics, like hide and seek, kiss chase (a canny chase game that you can deliberately engineer in order to end up alone with, and perhaps kissing, the boy you have a crush on) and piggy in the middle (two people play catch and a third, the poor piggy, has to try and steal whatever they are throwing, from the middle), there are some other, more unusual, games to play outdoors.

DOGGY, DOGGY, WHERE'S YOUR BONE?

✳ Decide who is to be the dog (i.e. 'it') and find a good tree stump or bench they can sit on. Next find the bone, a nice-looking natural object like a large pine cone, for example. The dog turns her back to everyone leaving the bone behind her and closes her eyes tightly. While she counts to fifty, someone steals the bone and hides it in their clothes. When the fifty is up and the dog turns round, everyone except the dog must chant:

'Doggy, doggy, where's your bone?
Somebody's stolen it from your home.
Guess who – it might be you.'

The dog must guess who took it by looking deeply into everyone's eyes to see if they can spot the guilty party. If the dog guesses wrong, the person who had the bone becomes the dog in the next round. If the dog guesses right, then she gets to be the dog again.

STUCK IN THE MUD

Somebody is chosen to be 'it'. Everyone moves around. If you are touched by the person who is 'it', you must remain stuck in the same spot with your legs wide apart in an A shape. You can only be released by someone crawling through your legs. If the person who is 'it' catches everyone, then they have won the game. If she gets tired and can't catch anyone, someone else can take over. As a rule, the last person to get stuck in the mud becomes 'it' next.

KICK THE CAN

* Once again, first choose someone to be 'it'. Their job is to protect the can (this can be a real can, or a ball, or a jumper), which is placed in an open space, and to run about trying to catch everyone else by touching them. If you are caught, you have to go and stand by the can. You must be freed by someone else kicking the can, obviously without getting touched by 'it'. If everyone is caught, the person who is 'it' has won. The last person to be caught becomes 'it' for the next game.

HONEY, IF YOU LOVE ME, SMILE

* Everyone sits down in a circle. Decide between you who is going to be 'it' and she then goes and stands in the middle of the circle. She asks

someone, 'Honey, do you love me?' at the same time making funny faces at her chosen victim or tickling them or sitting on their lap – anything to make them smile or laugh. The person being questioned must then answer, with a completely straight face, 'Honey, I love you but I just can't smile.' If they laugh or smile in any way before five minutes are up, then 'it' can impose a forfeit. She can choose whatever forfeit she likes, but here are some suggestions:

* sing a song
* kiss someone's bare feet
* quickly say a tongue-twister, five times over, for example: 'Six thick thistle sticks' or 'Three big blobs of a black bug's blood'
* give a two-minute talk about badgers
* answer 'yes' to a question asked by every other person playing
* dance a jig
* kiss everyone of the opposite sex who is also playing the game
* tell someone how much you love them and why in two minutes
* pretend to be a cat for two minutes
* do ten star jumps, five press-ups and five sit-ups

FANTASTIC FORFEITS

....
....
....
....
....
....
....
....
....
....
....
....
....
....
....
....
....
....
....
....
....
....
....
....

Painted Jars and Bottles

Don't throw away your used jars — instead make them beautiful and decorative simply by painting them. You can then use them to store anything from pens to pasta. You can find special glass or enamel paints in shops selling artists materials.

* old newspapers
* clean bottles or jam jars
* fine paint brush
* tracing paper
* chinagraph pencil
* masking tape
* enamel or specialist glass paints

* Always lay out lots of newspaper on the table or surface you will be working on and make sure the surface of the glass you are going to decorate is completely clean and dry before you start.

Simple shapes and patterns can be painted onto the glass freehand — spots, stripes, clouds, rainbows, little flowers, for example. For more complicated designs on wide-mouthed jam jars, trace the outline of your design onto paper, then

tape this to the inside of the glass and paint the outside by following the lines. If your bottle is too narrow to insert a traced design, you can use a greasy pencil like a chinagraph pencil to draw your design, then use paint to fill it in. Rub off the pencil marks once the paint is completely dry. In this way you can create handy labelled jars for the kitchen or bathroom. For a stripy effect, stick strips of masking tape on the jar and paint the clear glass between the pieces, then allow it to dry. When you remove the tape you will have created stripes with nice straight edges. For an extra glittering touch, while the paint is still wet, use tweezers to stick beads or sparkly sequins to your painted glass.

NB: Glass paint is not suitable for dishwashers. Clean your decorated jars and bottles gently with a damp cloth.

DESIGNING MY PAINTED BOTTLE

* Use this template to design your own painted bottle. That way you will have your design perfected before you begin on your bottle or jar.

Patchwork

Patchwork is a traditional way of joining scraps of material together to make something new. Even the simplest patchwork has a nice home-made charm but with just a little imagination (and quite a lot of patience) it's possible to make very intricate designs.

* It's important to use pieces of material of roughly the same thickness and it's best not to join very old, worn patches to very new ones. Patchwork is a great way to recycle old clothes you're fond of but don't want to throw out, or for showing off pretty pieces of material which, by themselves, are too small for anything useful. Keep a beady eye out when you're in charity shops for old shirts, scarves and dresses. If you only have a few large pieces of material to work with you could cut each large piece in half and dye one half a different colour (you could try using the blackberry dye from page 32). That way, the underlying weave and pattern will match, but you'll be able to mix up the different colours.

A PATCHWORK CUSHION

* Cut out a 10 x 10-centimetre square and a 12 x 12-centimetre square from cardboard, to use as templates. Make sure that these squares are perfect, or your patchwork won't fit together properly. Next, using the smaller template, cut out 9 squares from stiff paper (thick brown paper is good, or pages from a glossy magazine) then, using the larger template, cut 9 squares from your scraps of fabric. For each individual patch, place a paper square on the back of a fabric square and pin it together in the centre. Then, folding the edges of the fabric over the paper, tack them down (figure 1a). Make sure the folds are neat, so the material fits the paper lining exactly. Join the

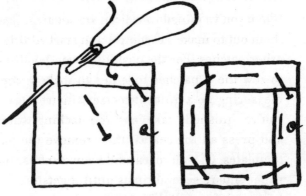

figure 1a

patches by placing two together, right sides facing, and oversewing along one side (figure 1b). Keep your stitches small and evenly spaced and at right angles to the join; try to catch just the very edge of the material and (as far as possible) don't sew through the paper shapes inside.

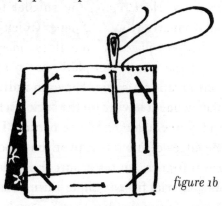

figure 1b

When you've joined your first two squares, flatten them out to make a rectangle and start adding the other patches. For the cushion cover, you'll need to sew the 9 patches together to make a square measuring 30 x 30 centimetres (figure 2). Once you've finished, take out the tacking stitches and press all the seams, then remove the paper templates (if you're careful, you can use each paper square several times until it gets too many holes in it from all the tacking).

figure 2

Sew another 9 squares together or, if you've had enough oversewing for the time being, measure a 31 x 31-centimetre square of plain fabric to form the back of your cushion and cut it out. The extra centimetre is for the seams. Flatten out the edges of your patchwork, then place the back and the front of your cushion together, right sides facing, and sew round three edges, using backstitch. Tie off the thread and turn the patchwork the right way round.

Now, you need to fill the cushion cover. If you have a ready-made cushion which is just the right size, well and good; otherwise, you can buy bags of polyester stuffing from department stores or craft shops, or else make a cushion pad by cutting squares out of an old fleece and sewing them roughly together round the edges. Fill the pad with stuffing. When the cushion cover is full, turn in the raw edges along the fourth side and oversew, to shut the seam. You could put some dried lavender flowers inside to make it smell nice – lavender is very soothing – so it would make a good pillow for your bedroom, to help you sleep peacefully at night.

Once you have mastered the basic patchwork technique, you can start experimenting with different shapes and patterns, as well as adding appliqué and decorative stitching. Try using triangles, rectangles, diamonds and hexagons. Sew lines of running stitch across plain patches using embroidery thread, or sew a button into the middle of each patch. You can make it as simple or as complicated as you like (figure 3).

figure 3

MY PATCHWORK PATTERN

notes

....
....
....
....
....
....
....
....
....
....
....
....
....
....
....
....
....
....
....
....
....
....

Rainbows and How to Make One

My heart leaps up when I behold
A rainbow in the sky:
So was it when my life began;
So is it now I am a man;
So be it when I shall grow old,
   Or let me die!...

   William Wordsworth, 'The Rainbow'

Life is like a rainbow. You need both the sun
and the rain to make the colours appear.

   Anon.

A rainbow appears when the sun is shining behind you and it is raining in front of you. When light travels in a straight line it is always clear (or white) but when light hits water it breaks into the colours of a rainbow. So, when the sun is out and it is raining, the sunlight shines through the millions of raindrops, refracting — or bending them — into a parallel arc of different colours.

RAINBOW FACTS

* A rainbow's colours always appear in the same order: red, orange, yellow, green, blue, indigo and violet. An easy mnemonic (aid to memory) to help you remember this sequence is: Richard Of York Gave Battle In Vain.

* From an aeroplane window, rainbows will appear as a complete circle.

* Animals have very poor colour vision and therefore can't see rainbows.

* We only see rainbows in the early morning or late afternoon because of the position of the sun.

* You will never be able to walk through the arc of a rainbow and come out the other side, and you will never be able to find treasure under a rainbow – sadly.

* However far you walk, the rainbow will always be in front of you, while your back is to the sun. And if your back wasn't to the sun, you wouldn't be able to see the rainbow!

HOW TO MAKE
YOUR OWN RAINBOW

* a sunny day
* a large deep saucepan
* a medium-sized mirror about 20 x 20cm
* white paper

Fill the saucepan with tap water then go outside and put the mirror upright, at the edge of the saucepan (you can fix it in place by propping it up with a big log or some bricks). Make sure the sun is shining directly into the mirror. Now, position the white paper so the reflection of the sunlight from the mirror shines onto it. Move the mirror around until you can see the water reflected in it from the saucepan and at the edge of this watery reflection you will see colours forming.

You have just created your own rainbow! You can also do this experiment inside by shining a torch into the mirror.

SAUCER RAINBOW

This simple scientific experiment is a way of making a totally different type of rainbow display indoors.

* clean saucer
* milk
* food colouring – red, yellow, blue, green
* washing-up liquid

✳ Fill a saucer with milk. Add a tiny drop of different food colouring to the milk round the compass points of the saucer – red and green on one side, blue and yellow, on the other, for example. Carefully put one tiny drip of washing-up liquid into the centre of the milk. You will immediately see a wondrous, changing pattern of colours merging and separating on the milk as the washing-up liquid breaks the surface tension allowing the food dyes to mix and mingle, forming different rainbow colours as they combine.

crumptious
Sweets and Treats

These home-made sweets are fun to make and look very professional. Before you start, wash your hands extra well. If you don't have any small cutters, use the well-washed screw top from a small bottle or jar to cut out round sweets. You can buy tiny foil or paper cases for the sweets to add to the attractiveness of the finished delights.

COCONUT ICE

MAKES APPROX. 35—40 SMALL CUBES

* 400g icing sugar
* 1—2 tbsp milk
* white of an egg
* 100g desiccated coconut
* two drops pink food colouring

Sieve the sugar into a bowl then add the coconut and mix together. Add 1 tablespoon of milk and stir well.

In a separate bowl, whip the egg white until frothy but not stiff. Gradually add the egg white to the coconut mixture until it forms a soft paste. If the paste is too firm, add a little more milk, drop by drop, until the paste is soft enough to spread.

Line a shallow baking tray with greaseproof paper and spread half the coconut ice onto it.

Add the food colouring to the remaining mixture until the colour becomes even and pale pink. Spread this onto the white ice then press lightly with the back of a wooden spoon so the two layers stick together. Leave overnight in a warm place to set. Then either use a cutter to make small individual sweets or cut into squares and put into paper cases.

ERMINT CREAMS

APPROX. 40—45 SWEETS

* walnut-sized knob of butter, softened
* 1 tbsp single cream
* ½ tsp peppermint essence
* 200g icing sugar, more if necessary
* 3—5 drops green food colouring (optional)

* Sieve the icing sugar onto a plate. Put the butter into a mixing bowl and add the cream and peppermint essence. Mix well until completely smooth and lump free. Gradually add the sugar, mixing each addition well with a wooden spoon each time to blend, until you have a very stiff paste. You may need to add more icing sugar if the paste is too sticky to handle. Dust your hands with sugar and use them to knead the paste to make it smooth and firm. Divide it in two, leaving one half in the bowl. Lightly dust a board or clean work surface with a little icing sugar, and roll out the paste evenly until it is about a centimetre in thickness. Cut into small sweet-sized rounds, using a small sweet cutter, or a screw bottle top if you don't have a cutter small enough. Put the sweets on greaseproof paper dusted with a little

icing sugar. Leave to dry and harden, turning over after a couple of hours to allow the underside to dry. If you want green peppermints add a few drops of food colouring to the remaining paste to tint it delicately, then roll, cut out the sweets and leave to dry as above.

For a pretty and professional presentation, put the peppermints in small individual paper cases, then arrange, alternating white and green mints, in a box or on a plate

BUTTERSCOTCH

The bubbling sugar syrup in this and the next recipe is extremely hot, so it's probably best to make this with an adult to help you.

* 150g brown sugar
* 100g butter
* 1½ teacups golden syrup
* 1 tsp vanilla essence
* pinch bicarbonate of soda
* 3 tsp vinegar
* pinch salt

Melt the butter in a saucepan and add the sugar, golden syrup, bicarbonate of soda, vinegar and salt. Bring to the boil and leave to bubble for about ten to fifteen minutes. Test to see if the butterscotch is ready by dropping a small amount from a spoon into a glass of cold water, being extra careful not to burn yourself as it will be very hot. If it sets and is brittle enough to break, it is ready. Stir in the vanilla essence, pour into a baking tray lined with greaseproof paper. When slightly cooled and beginning to harden, cut the butterscotch into squares with an oiled knife.

HELENSBOROUGH TOFFEE

This is an old Scottish recipe for a toffee that is, strictly speaking, a delicious and buttery, crumbly fudge.

* 100g butter
* 800g brown sugar
* 1 teacup milk
* 1 large tin condensed milk
* 3–4 drops vanilla essence

Line a shallow rectangular baking tin with some greaseproof paper.

Melt the butter in a saucepan over a gentle heat then add the sugar and milk. Bring to the boil and allow to simmer gently, stirring all the while, for 10 minutes.

Add the condensed milk. Simmer for a further 20 minutes, stirring all the time. This is a lot of stirring, but it's very important not to get bored and stop or the mixture will stick to the pan and burn. Don't worry if it looks very pale and milky – after 20 minutes it turns a beautiful pale caramel colour. When this happens, remove the toffee from the heat and stir in the vanilla essence.

Pour into the baking tin and allow to cool. When the toffee is almost set, mark it into squares with a knife so it will break easily when it is ready.

Shadow Puppets

Making shadow puppets on the wall with your hands is great fun. All you need is a source of light, your hands and a clear wall as a backdrop. For an extra evocative touch, use a candle rather than an electric table lamp or torch.

* Hold your hands about 60 centimetres from the light source. The wall that you will be projecting onto should be about a metre away.

FLYING BIRD

* Move your hands backwards and forwards to make the bird fly.

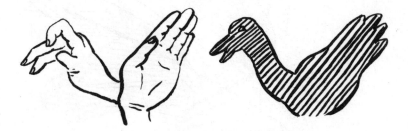

RUNNING RABBIT

* Wiggle the bottom fingers to make the rabbit run.

HORSE

* Practise moving your arms and hands up and down gracefully to make the horse gallop.

CROCODILE

* Snap your hands together holding your wrists still to make the crocodile bite.

Sherbet Surprise SERVES 4

You can of course buy sherbet dabs in some sweet shops, but making sherbet yourself is more satisfying and the finished product has much more zing. Citric acid is used as a preservative and food flavouring — it can usually be found in old-fashioned chemist shops.

* 7 tsp icing sugar
* 3 tsp citric acid
* 1 tsp bicarbonate of soda

Sieve the icing sugar into a small mixing bowl and stir in the citric acid and bicarbonate of soda. The citric acid is slightly gritty, so grind all the ingredients together with the back of a wooden spoon until you have a fine powder.

Taste immediately by dipping a fruit lolly or some liquorice in the sherbet and enjoy the fizz on your tongue. You can also spoon it over ice cream or add it to water for a refreshing drink. Store any leftover sherbet in a clean airtight container.

If you want to make individual presents to put in goody bags at a birthday party, make a larger quantity by simply using tablespoons of the ingredients in the same proportions.

Shortbread Stars and Hearts   MAKES 15-20

Everyone loves a home-made gift and these are perfect — use pastry cutters to make pretty star- and heart-shaped biscuits. When cooked, put them into paper or clear cellophane bags and tie them with ribbon for birthday presents or take them to your host when invited for tea. The cornflour is the ingredient that gives this shortbread its irresistible crunch.

* 200g soft butter
* 100g caster sugar
* 200g plain flour
* 100g cornflour or rice flour

Preheat the oven to 160°C/gas mark 3.

In a bowl mix together the butter and sugar and beat vigorously until creamy and pale coloured. Add the flour and cornflour gradually, and stir with a wooden spoon until well mixed. Turn on to a floured board, and knead gently until smooth. Lightly dust a rolling pin with flour, then roll out the shortbread paste evenly until about 5 millimetres to a centimetre thick. Cut into biscuit shapes, and put on a baking tray lined with greaseproof paper.

Cook for about 20 to 30 minutes. The biscuits will have turned slightly golden round the edges, but will still be soft when you take them out of the oven. Don't worry. They harden and crisp as they cool. Prick the biscuits softly with a fork, then sprinkle finely with caster sugar. Leave them to cool completely, then put them in bags for gifts or store them in an airtight container to maintain the crunch.

A Simple Skirt

This is a very pretty, very simple, wrap-around skirt. It doesn't involve anything tricky like buttons or zips so it's easy to sew, and you can make it any length you please. Whether it's long or short, this skirt looks so nice you'll want to wear it all the time. To make a knee-length skirt, you will need:

* 2m piece of fabric
* 2m length of broad ribbon c. 3cm wide, for the waistband
* felt-tipped pen
* string
* 3.5m length of narrow ribbon c. 1cm wide, for the hem (optional)
* needle, thread
* scissors
* tape measure

Spread the fabric flat on the floor, with the patterned side facing up, and fold it in half so you have a square with the back or reverse of the fabric showing. Fold the square in half diagonally so you have a triangle with the folded edge at the

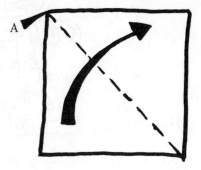

figure 1a

top (figure 1a). Next, you need to mark the waist and bottom edge of the skirt. Measure your waist (if you're wearing a thick jumper, make sure to take it off first, or else the finished skirt will end up loose and in danger of falling down!). Use the chart on the next page to work out how wide the waistline should be (this is shown by the distance from A to B, see figure 1b). Choose the waist measurement closest to yours (if you're right between two, always use the smaller one).

figure 1b

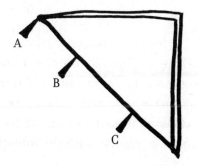

WAIST	A to B
50cm	30cm
55cm	33cm
60cm	36cm
65cm	39cm
70cm	42cm
75cm	45cm
80cm	48cm
85cm	51cm

✳ Making very sure your fabric is the right way
up (there should be one folded layer and two
single ones along the top, and four single,
non-folded layers down the right-hand side),
carefully measure out the distance from A to B
along the longest, diagonal edge, and make a
mark with your pen. To work out the length of
the skirt (B to C), use your tape measure to
measure from your waist down to your knee.
(It's surprisingly difficult to do this, because
you have to bend over to read the tape measure:

try stretching down and putting a finger against your knee to hold the tape measure in place before you read it; otherwise, you could ask a passing person for help.) When you've got the right length, measure the fabric, making very sure to start measuring from the mark you made for the waist at B and not from the corner. Make another mark with your pen (C). This pattern is for a knee-length skirt: if you'd like a longer skirt, just work out the length you'd like, and measure that distance from B to C instead. Be warned, though – longer skirts take up a lot more material: you'd need a piece of fabric approximately 1.5 x 3 metres for an ankle-length skirt, and about 5 metres of narrow ribbon to trim the hem.

Once you've marked up the measurements for the waist and the hem, you need to draw two arcs. To do this, tie the string about halfway up the pen. Put the tip of the pen on the first mark at B and – holding the pen straight up, at right-angles to the fabric – stretch the string back to the corner of your triangle at A. Put your thumb firmly on the string to hold it in place, right on the corner, and – keeping the pen

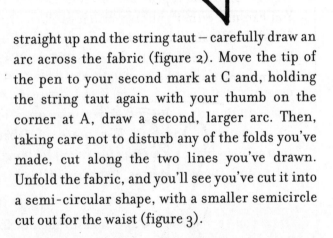

figure 2

straight up and the string taut – carefully draw an arc across the fabric (figure 2). Move the tip of the pen to your second mark at C and, holding the string taut again with your thumb on the corner at A, draw a second, larger arc. Then, taking care not to disturb any of the folds you've made, cut along the two lines you've drawn. Unfold the fabric, and you'll see you've cut it into a semi-circular shape, with a smaller semicircle cut out for the waist (figure 3).

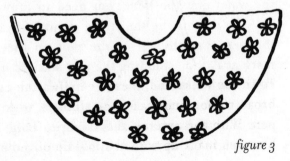

figure 3

Now, it's time to start sewing. First, open out the material and hem the straight edges. With the reverse of the fabric facing you, make a 1-centimetre fold along the right-hand edge, then make a second fold, 2 centimetres wide. Pin the folds in place and sew along the inside edge (figure 4), then repeat on the left-hand side. You can use either running stitch or backstitch for this. Because you'll be sewing quite long hems, don't make the stitches too tiny — neat 1-centimetre stitches are fine.

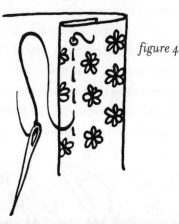

figure 4

To fit the waistband, measure halfway along the broad ribbon and make a small mark with your pen. With the reverse of the fabric facing you, line this mark up with the middle of the small semicircle: this is your starting point. Carefully sew the top edge of the ribbon along the top edge of your skirt. You should use running stitch for this, and sew about 2–3 millimetres in, just enough so the fabric doesn't pull through. When you reach the end, go back to the middle point, and sew along the other half. (There should be a good length of ribbon left over at either side – don't cut this off; you'll need it to tie the skirt round your waist). Carefully fold the ribbon over the top of the seam you've made round the waistline and down again over the front of the skirt, so the cut edge of the fabric is folded neatly inside and the ribbon is lying flat against the patterned side of the material. Using running stitch, sew along the bottom edge of the ribbon to hold it in place. When you've finished, you should have a pretty waistband with a tie at either side (figure 5).

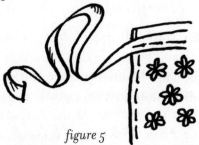

figure 5

If you want to, you can use this same technique to sew a narrow ribbon along the bottom of the skirt, to give it a neat edge (you should cut the excess ribbon off though, leaving just 2 centimetres to fold over and sew in place). You can always leave the bottom edge of your skirt raw if you prefer – because it's cut on a slant, it won't fray as much as a straight edge would, so you can get away without hemming it. If you like, you can sew along the bottom using whipped running stitch (see page 69). There's enough material left over to add a pocket or two, if you want: for each pocket, cut a rectangle of fabric 16 x 20 centimetres, hem one shorter edge, fold the other edges under by a centimetre and tack the folds down using running stitch, then try your skirt on and pin the pockets in the right position (it's different for everyone) before sewing them on using backstitch. Remember to remove the tacking stitches once they're properly attached.

When you've finished, wrap your skirt round your waist twice, tie the ribbons in a secure bow at the side to hold it firmly in place, put your hands in your pockets and you're good to go!

Growing Tomatoes

The only thing better than eating juicy ripe tomatoes, fresh from the vine, is knowing you've grown them yourself. It's amazingly easy to do, and if you don't have a garden, you can grow them on a roof or windowsill. Home-grown tomatoes have a much better flavour than those raised commercially and if you choose the right variety the plants should keep producing fruit throughout the summer. And yes, a tomato is, strictly speaking, a fruit and not a vegetable!

You need to sow the seeds in the first week of April, in order to plant the young seedlings into pots in early June. Try to get variety called Sweet 100, which you should be able to find in any garden centre. If you can't find these, make sure you buy another cordon type, since these are the easiest tomatoes to grow in pots. They'll be producing tomatoes by the end of August all the way through to the end of September if you look after the plants carefully.

* packet tomato seeds
* compartmentalized seed tray
* small bag vermiculite
* medium bag good multi-purpose compost
* 4 plastic pots (6cm wide)
* 4 bamboo canes (about 1m high)
* watering can with a fine sprinkling
  nozzle on its spout
* 4 terracotta pots (or any other pots
  no smaller than 20cm wide)
* liquid tomato fertilizer, organic if possible
* pencil

✳ Fill the seed tray with moist compost. Sow a seed in each of the compartments – you'll probably need to sow about twelve seeds in order to ensure you get four good plants. Cover the seeds thinly with a light dusting of vermiculite and then a little more compost, water with a small sprinkle of water from your watering can and place the tray on a windowsill. Keep watering the trays regularly, little but often, so the compost is always moist but never waterlogged.

In about six weeks, by mid-May, the seedlings should be growing nicely. Choose the strongest-looking plants, discarding any wimpy ones, and use a pencil to loosen them from the soil, very gently lifting them out of the seed tray by a leaf. Fill the plastic pots with compost and water the compost well. Wait for the water to drain and then make a hole in the centre of the compost with your pencil. Plant the seedlings right up to their first leaves. Keep these pots inside on the windowsill, or on the floor beneath a sunny window. Once again, water regularly – a little every day if it is hot weather, every few days if it's not – always keeping the soil moist but not waterlogged. Keep the pots on a tray to catch the excess water as it runs through to avoid ruining your windowsill or carpet.

When the first white flowers appear, prise the plants and their roots very carefully out of the small pots and transfer them into the bigger pots you've already filled with compost and watered as before. Be very careful not to bruise the plant at this stage. Plant the tomato up to the first set of leaves and press the compost down firmly with your fingers so it's snug in its new home. Place a bamboo cane in each pot, next to the plant, and tie the plant to it loosely with string. You want the main shoot to grow up the cane, so keep tying the plant to the cane as it grows. Water regularly – never over-water. At this point it should be early June and you can transfer the pots outside and put them against a sunny, if possible

south-facing, wall, balcony or roof terrace. Water every day if it's a hot summer. And note that if it is very hot and sunny you should only water in the early morning or evening, when the sun is not shining directly on them, otherwise you might harm the plants.

You will need to prune your tomatoes by removing the suckers which grow in the angle where the branches leave the main stem. This will ensure that the plant produces the best possible tomatoes. And if you see little weeds growing in the pot, just pull them out. Feed the plants about once a week, following the instructions on the packet.

It is, of course, obvious when the tomatoes are ripe and ready, since they will become a beautiful deep red colour. Pick them with the calyx (the green star-shaped base) still attached.

Turn Milk into Plastic

This is an interesting scientific experiment — by just boiling some milk with a few teaspoons of vinegar you can make a weird jelly-like plastic substance which can then be kneaded and modelled to make beads and brooches or even decorations for a Christmas tree.

* 1 cup full-fat milk
* small saucepan
* teaspoon
* white wine vinegar
* clean jam jar
* greaseproof paper

* Pour the milk into the pan, add 2 teaspoons of vinegar and heat. Keep stirring. When the mixture boils, it will form tiny lumps (curds) in a clear

liquid (whey). Strain the liquid through a sieve and spoon the curds into the jam jar. The acetic acid in the vinegar separates the protein casein from the milk. Casein is an ingredient used to make plastic – thus plastic milk!

Add a teaspoon of vinegar to the curds, and let it stand for a couple of hours. The curds will form a yellowish blob at the bottom of a clear liquid. The blob consists of animal fat, minerals and the casein. Pour off the liquid, remove the rubbery blob from the jar and gently rinse it with water, then knead it until it has the consistency of dough and mould it into any shape you wish. Dry it on the greaseproof paper overnight. The casein will harden into plastic and can be painted with acrylic paints. You could make a heart shape and carefully pierce a hole through the top with a knitting needle then string a ribbon through the hole and hang the heart from a Christmas tree or wear it as a pendant.

Rubber Egg

This is another scientific transformation trick — to make a bouncy ball from a boiled egg.

* hard-boiled egg in its shell
* clean empty jam jar with lid
* white wine vinegar

* Put the egg in the jar and cover with vinegar. Screw on the lid and leave for a week and you are left with a rubbery egg that will bounce, if not dropped from too great a height. The hard eggshell turns to rubber in the vinegar because acetic acid dissolves the calcium carbonate from which the eggshell is made.

Wild Bees in Your Garden

There are over 20,000 species of bee in the world. You may have seen some in your garden — little yellow honey bees, big fuzzy bumble bees, burrowing mason bees, even leaf-cutter and wool-carder bees. These wild bees won't make honey for you, but having them around helps a garden to thrive because they fertilize the flowers, so it's important to do whatever you can to make them feel welcome. Wild bees live in burrows, nests and holes. To encourage them into your garden, keep a pile of stones, bits of wood and empty snail shells in a quiet corner for the bees to find and make nests.

If you want to go a step further, why not make a bee box?

BEE BOX

* All you need to make your bee box is a block of wood 30 x 15 x 15 centimetres, and a drill for making holes (please ask a sensible grown-up to help you — drills can do a lot of damage in the

wrong hands). It's best to use a bit of old, untreated wood: if you use a new piece, you might have to leave it to weather for a while before the bees will move in. Drill a dozen or so holes in the front of the wood, 4–10 millimetres in diameter and at least 10 centimetres deep (don't drill right through the wood, though). Leave at least 2 centimetres between each hole, and drill them in a random pattern, rather than in neat lines. Make the holes at a slight angle, sloping upwards so that the inside stays dry – you can add a roof, if you like, which sticks out a bit over the front (figure 1). Fix your box 100–150 centimetres high on a south-facing wall or a tree, somewhere where it's in direct sunlight, and wait for the bees to set up home!

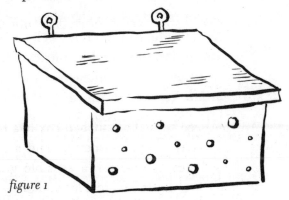

figure 1

figure 2

BEE LOG

* If you don't have access to a drill, you can make
a bee log instead, using hollow bamboo canes or
drinking straws 5–10 millimetres in diameter.
(Use paper straws if you can find them, rather
than plastic ones – some bees divide their
burrows up into separate chambers using mud,
and the mud doesn't stick so well to plastic.)
Next, find a straight-sided cylindrical container,
7–10 centimetres in diameter and at least
10 centimetres deep. A tin can will do (paint it
green first, to camouflage it and stop it from
rusting); otherwise, you could cut down a plastic
drinking bottle. Cut the canes or straws to the
right length and pack them closely inside your
container, filling in any gaps so they won't slide

out. Make sure the end of each tube is tightly pressed against the bottom of the container. Tie some twine round your bee log and fix it firmly to a wall or the branch of a tree, in a sunny spot, where it's sheltered from the worst of the weather and won't get blown around too much (figure 2).

FLOWERS BEES LIKE

You can also attract bees to your garden by making sure there are lots of flowers for them. Bees like:

* lavender
* forget-me-nots
* apple blossom
* daisies
* thyme
* foxgloves

* cherry blossom
* buttercups
* heather
* hollyhocks
* lime blossom
* and, especially, clover

Best of all, bees love weeds: dandelions, rosebay willow herb, brambles and nettles are all firm favourites. Find a place that's really overgrown, then sit back on a sunny summer's day and watch the bees come and go.

Writing a Letter

Everyone loves the sound of a plump envelope, with a handwritten letter inside, coming through the letter box – especially when the handwritten address has your name on it! Find a pen-pal and get your writing paper out, and remember, the more letters you send, the more likely you are to receive replies.

LETTER-WRITING TIPS

* Write as neatly as you can and take care with paragraphs, punctuation and spelling – reading your letter shouldn't be hard work for whoever you're sending it to. Play around with the types of paper you use. You can make your own cards, decorate a plain piece of paper or even make your own postcards.

  If the letter is to a friend or your granny, for example, it doesn't need to sound too formal. Write from your heart. Write exactly what you would tell your friend if you were talking on the telephone – things that made you happy or sad, or something that has upset you. Write about your dreams or nightmares, if they are odd and amusing. Write some good jokes, if you've heard some funny ones that make you laugh. Ask questions, so your friend will write back with the answers. And, most importantly, when writing your letter, be as entertaining and descriptive as you can – the joy of a really good letter is in the detail. A description of your day at school need not be dull as long as you add lots of amusing details – a teacher with an oddly shaped nose; a particularly unpleasant lunch with slimy cabbage, or lumpy custard with a thick skin on top – all these will liven up what at first might seem like a very ordinary day.

PEOPLE TO WRITE LETTERS TO

name

sort of letter

A THANK YOU LETTER

Dearest Aunt Flo

Thank you so much for the wonderful flower press you gave me. [A few specifics go down well.] *I have already filled it with daisies from the garden, and Mum says that when her pansies come out I can have a few of those too.* [A little polite enquiry never goes amiss.] *I hope your ankle is better — I feel awful about you slipping on that spilt jelly.* [And, finally, a cheery sign-off.] *Do send my love to Uncle Thomas, and hope to see you both really soon.*

x x x

write your sample letter here

Make Your Own Yoghurt

Think how nice it would be invite friends over for a breakfast of home-made yoghurt and blackberries you've picked yourself! Much more fun than boring old cereal and delicious too. This will make enough to fill a large bowl.

* ½ litre full-fat milk
* saucepan
* 1 tbsp live natural yoghurt
* large mixing bowl
* wooden spoon
* large plate or clingfilm to cover
* woollen blanket or shawl

First, bring the milk to the boil in a saucepan. As soon as it bubbles, turn the heat right down and let it simmer very gently for 2 minutes. Remove the pan from the heat and leave the milk to cool just long enough so you can barely dip your finger in. DO NOT do this yourself — ask an adult to test the temperature for you! The milk must be hot enough to cause a mild stinging sensation — too hot or too cold and the yoghurt won't set.

Put the yoghurt in the large bowl and beat it with a wooden spoon until it is very runny, then add the hot milk a little at a time, beating each addition well. Cover the bowl with a plate or clingfilm and wrap it up in a woollen blanket or shawl to keep it warm.

Leave the bowl in a warm place well away from draughts (an airing cupboard is ideal) overnight or for at least 12 hours, until the yoghurt has set. Don't forget about your yoghurt – if left for much longer than 12 hours it will lose its creaminess and become sharp in taste. Store the yoghurt in the fridge for up to a week.

Chop up some soft fruits such as strawberries and raspberries, or add stewed rhubarb and gooseberries to make flavoured yoghurts.

THINGS I'VE DONE

notes

THINGS I'D LIKE TO DO

notes

notes

ACKNOWLEDGMENTS

Firstly and most importantly, thank you to Claire Paterson and Kirsty Gordon, for their inspiration, quirky creativity and all-round gloriousness.

I am indebted to my son Spike Lacey for his editorial finesse and ideas, his help with toffee making and tasting, and the exploding experiments. And to Arzu Tahsin and Florence Lacey, Hackney's most beautiful and funny domestic goddesses.

Thanks also to Bryan Nelder of Gayhurst Community School in Hackney for his scientific genius and ideas. And to Clio Marsden and Joy Haney.

To Tif Loehnis, Jenny McVeigh and Tim Glister at Janklow & Nesbit. And once again to the brilliant editors, designers and friends at Penguin: Jenny Dean, Eleo Gordon, Venetia Butterfield, Sarah Fraser, Yeti McCaldin, Keith Taylor and Liz Davis. And Natacha Ledwidge for the beautiful illustrations.

The Great Big Glorious Book For Girls

Rosemary Davidson
Sarah Vine

The number one bestselling guide for girls
of every age

'Packed with games, recipes, beauty hints,
gardening tips, inspiring quotes and infinite
ways of passing time, it's designed to appeal
to the girl in every one of us' *Women and Home*